Michael Starbird, Ph.D.

University Distinguished Teaching Professor of Mathematics,
The University of Texas at Austin

Michael Starbird is Professor of Mathematics and a University Distinguished Teaching Professor at The University of Texas at Austin. He received his B.A. degree from Pomona College in 1970 and his Ph.D. in mathematics from the University of Wisconsin, Madison, in 1974. That same year, he joined the faculty of the Department of Mathematics of The University of Texas at Austin, where he has stayed, except for leaves as a Visiting Member of the Institute for Advanced Study in Princeton, New Jersey; a Visiting Associate Professor at the University of California, San Diego; and a member of the technical staff at the Jet Propulsion Laboratory in Pasadena, California.

Professor Starbird served as Associate Dean in the College of Natural Sciences at The University of Texas at Austin from 1989 to 1997. He is a member of the Academy of Distinguished Teachers at UT. He has won many teaching awards, including the Mathematical Association of America's Deborah and Franklin Tepper Haimo Award for Distinguished College or University Teaching of Mathematics, which is awarded to three professors annually from among the 27,000 members of the MAA; a Minnie Stevens Piper Professorship, which is awarded each year to 10 professors from any subject at any college or university in the state of Texas; the inaugural award of the Dad's Association Centennial Teaching Fellowship; the Excellence Award from the Eyes of Texas, twice; the President's Associates Teaching Excellence Award; the Jean Holloway Award for Teaching Excellence, which is the oldest teaching award at UT and is presented to one professor each year; the Chad Oliver Plan II Teaching Award, which is student-selected and awarded each year to one professor in the Plan II liberal arts honors program; and the Friar Society Centennial Teaching Fellowship, which is awarded to one professor at UT annually and includes the largest monetary teaching prize given at UT. Also, in 1989, Professor Starbird was the Recreational Sports Super Racquets Champion.

The professor's mathematical research is in the field of topology. He recently served as a member-at-large of the Council of the American Mathematical Society and on the national education committees of both the

American Mathematical Society and the Mathematical Association of America.

Professor Starbird is interested in bringing authentic understanding of significant ideas in mathematics to people who are not necessarily mathematically oriented. He has developed and taught an acclaimed class that presents higher-level mathematics to liberal arts students. He wrote, with co-author Edward B. Burger, *The Heart of Mathematics: An invitation to effective thinking*, which won a 2001 Robert W. Hamilton Book Award. Professors Burger and Starbird have also written a book that brings intriguing mathematical ideas to the public, entitled *Coincidences, Chaos, and All That Math Jazz: Making Light of Weighty Ideas*, published by W.W. Norton, 2005. Professor Starbird has produced three previous courses for The Teaching Company, the first edition of *Change and Motion: Calculus Made Clear*; *Meaning from Data: Statistics Made Clear*; and with collaborator Edward Burger, *The Joy of Thinking: The Beauty and Power of Classical Mathematical Ideas*. Professor Starbird loves to see real people find the intrigue and fascination that mathematics can bring.

Change and Motion: Calculus Made Clear, 2nd Edition
Parts I & II
Michael Starbird, Ph.D.

PUBLISHED BY:

THE TEACHING COMPANY
4151 Lafayette Center Drive, Suite 100
Chantilly, Virginia 20151-1232
1-800-TEACH-12
Fax—703-378-3819
www.teach12.com

Acknowledgments

I want to thank Alex Pekker for his excellent help with every aspect of this second edition of the calculus course. Alex collaborated with me substantially on the design of the whole course, on the examples and flow of the individual lectures, on the design of the graphics, and on the written materials. Thanks also to Professor Katherine Socha for her work on the first edition of this course and for her help during the post-production process of the second edition. Thanks to Alisha Reay, Pam Greer, Lucinda Robb, Noreen Nelson, and others from The Teaching Company not only for their excellent professional work during the production of this series of lectures but also for creating a supportive and enjoyable atmosphere in which to work. Thanks to my wife, Roberta Starbird, for her design and construction of several of the props. Finally, thanks to Roberta and my children, Talley and Bryn, for their special encouragement.

Table of Contents
Change and Motion: Calculus Made Clear, 2nd Edition

Professor Biography i
Course Scope 1
Lecture One   Two Ideas, Vast Implications............................ 4
Lecture Two   Stop Sign Crime—The First Idea
                           of Calculus—The Derivative 10
Lecture Three   Another Car, Another Crime—
                           The Second Idea of Calculus—The Integral.... 15
Lecture Four   The Fundamental Theorem of Calculus........... 20
Lecture Five   Visualizing the Derivative—Slopes................. 25
Lecture Six   Derivatives the Easy Way—
                           Symbol Pushing 31
Lecture Seven   Abstracting the Derivative—
                           Circles and Belts 37
Lecture Eight   Circles, Pyramids, Cones, and Spheres............ 44
Lecture Nine   Archimedes and the Tractrix............................ 48
Lecture Ten   The Integral and the Fundamental Theorem 52
Lecture Eleven   Abstracting the Integral—
                           Pyramids and Dams 60
Lecture Twelve   Buffon's Needle or π from Breadsticks 64
Lecture Thirteen   Achilles, Tortoises, Limits, and Continuity 70
Lecture Fourteen   Calculators and Approximations...................... 75
Lecture Fifteen   The Best of All Possible Worlds—
                           Optimization 80
Lecture Sixteen   Economics and Architecture 85
Lecture Seventeen   Galileo, Newton, and Baseball........................ 90
Lecture Eighteen   Getting off the Line—Motion in Space 95
Lecture Nineteen   Mountain Slopes and Tangent Planes 99
Lecture Twenty   Several Variables—Volumes Galore 103
Lecture Twenty-One   The Fundamental Theorem Extended............ 107

Table of Contents
Change and Motion: Calculus Made Clear, 2nd Edition

Lecture Twenty-Two   Fields of Arrows—Differential Equations..... 112

Lecture Twenty-Three   Owls, Rats, Waves, and Guitars..................... 118

Lecture Twenty-Four   Calculus Everywhere 123

Timeline 127

Glossary 130

Biographical Notes.. 135

Bibliography.. 141

Change and Motion: Calculus Made Clear, 2nd Edition

Scope:

Twenty-five hundred years ago, the Greek philosopher Zeno watched an arrow speeding toward its target and framed one of the most productive paradoxes in the history of human thought. He posed the paradox of motion: Namely, at every moment, the arrow is in only one place, yet it moves. This paradox evokes questions about the infinite divisibility of position and time. Two millennia later, Zeno's paradox was resolved with the invention of calculus, one of the triumphs of the human intellect.

Calculus has been one of the most influential ideas in human history. Its impact on our daily lives is incalculable, even with calculus. Economics, population growth, traffic flow, money matters, electricity, baseball, cosmology, and many other topics are modeled and explained using the ideas and the language of calculus. Calculus is also a fascinating intellectual adventure that allows us to see our world differently.

The deep concepts of calculus can be understood without the technical background traditionally required in calculus courses. Indeed, frequently, the technicalities in calculus courses completely submerge the striking, salient insights that compose the true significance of the subject. The concepts and insights at the heart of calculus are absolutely meaningful, understandable, and accessible to all intelligent people—regardless of the level or age of their previous mathematical experience.

Calculus is the exploration of two ideas, both of which arise from a clear, commonsensical analysis of our everyday experience of motion: the *derivative* and the *integral*. After an introduction, the course begins with a discussion of a car driving down a road. As we discuss velocity and position, these two foundational concepts of calculus arise naturally, and their relationship to each other becomes clear and convincing. Calculus directly describes and deals with motion. But the ideas developed there also present us with a dynamic view of the world based on a clear analysis of change. That perspective lets us view even such static objects as circles in a dynamic way—growing by accretion of infinitely thin layers. The pervasive nature of change makes calculus extremely widely applicable.

The course proceeds by exploring the rich variations and applications of the two fundamental ideas of calculus. After the introduction in the setting of motion, we proceed to develop the concepts of calculus from several points of view. We see the ideas geometrically and graphically. We interpret calculus ideas in terms of familiar formulas for areas and volumes. We see how the ideas developed in the simple setting of a car moving in a straight line can be extended to apply to motion in space. Among the many variations of the concepts of calculus, we see how calculus describes the contours of mountains and other three-dimensional objects. Finally, we explore the use of calculus in describing the physical, biological, and even architectural worlds.

One of the bases for the power of calculus lies in the fact that many questions in many subjects are equivalent when viewed at the appropriate level of abstraction. That is, the mathematical structures that one creates to study and model motion are identical, mathematically, to the structures that model phenomena from biology to economics, from traffic flow to cosmology. By looking at the mathematics itself, we strip away the extraneous features of the questions and focus on the underlying relationships and structures that govern the behavior of the system in question. Calculus is the mathematical structure that lies at the core of a world of seemingly unrelated issues.

It is in the language of calculus that scientists describe what we know of physical reality and how we express that knowledge. The language of calculus contains its share of mathematical symbols and terminology. However, we will see that every calculus idea and symbol can be understood in English, not requiring "mathese." We will not eschew formulas altogether, but we will make clear that every equation is an English sentence that has a meaning in English, and we will deal with that meaning in English. Indeed, one of the principal goals of this series of lectures is to have viewers understand the concepts of calculus as meaningful ideas, not as the manipulation of meaningless symbols.

Our daily experience of life at the beginning of the third millennium contrasts markedly with life in the 17th century. Most of the differences emerged from technical advances that rely on calculus. We live differently now because we can manipulate and control nature better than we could 300 years ago. That practical, predictive understanding of the physical processes of nature is largely enabled by the power and perspective of calculus. Calculus not only provides specific tools that solve practical problems, but it also entails an intellectual perspective on how we analyze the world.

Calculus is all around us and is a landmark achievement of humans that can be enjoyed and appreciated by all.

Lecture One
Two Ideas, Vast Implications

Scope: Calculus is the exploration of two ideas that arise from a clear, commonsensical analysis of everyday experience. But explorations of these ideas—the *derivative* and the *integral*—help us construct the very foundation of what we know of physical reality and how we express that knowledge. Many questions in many subjects are equivalent when viewed at the appropriate level of abstraction. That is, the mathematical structures that one creates to study and model motion are identical, mathematically, to the structures that model aspects of economics, population growth, traffic flow, fluid flow, electricity, baseball, planetary motion, and countless other topics. By looking at the mathematics itself, we strip away the extraneous features of the questions and focus on the underlying relationships and structures that govern and describe our world. Calculus has been one of the most effective conceptual tools in human history.

Outline

I. Calculus is all around us.

   A. When we're driving down a road and see where we are and how fast we are going…that's calculus.

   B. When we throw a baseball and see where it lands…that's calculus.

   C. When we see the planets and how they orbit around the Sun…that's calculus.

   D. When we lament the decline in the population of the spotted owl…that's calculus.

   E. When we analyze the stock market…that's calculus.

II. Calculus is an idea of enormous importance and historical impact.

   A. Calculus has been extremely effective in allowing people to bend nature to human purpose.

   B. In the 20th century, calculus has also become an essential tool for understanding social and biological sciences: It occurs every day in the description of economic trends, population growth, and medical treatments.

C. The physical world and how it works are described using calculus—its terms, its notation, its perspective.

D. To understand the history of the last 300 years, we must understand calculus. The technological developments in recent centuries are the story of this time, and many of those developments depend on calculus.

E. Why is calculus so effective? Because it resolves some basic issues associated with change and motion.

III. Twenty-five hundred years ago, the philosopher Zeno pointed out the paradoxical nature of motion. Zeno's paradoxes confront us with questions about motion. Calculus resolves these ancient conundrums.

A. Two of Zeno's paradoxes of motion involve an arrow in flight.
  1. The first is the *arrow paradox*: If at every moment, the arrow is at a particular point, then at every moment, it is at rest at a point.
  2. The second is the *dichotomy paradox*: To reach its target, an arrow must first fly halfway, then half the remaining distance, then half the remaining distance, and so on, forever. Because it must move an infinite number of times, it will never reach the target.

B. Looking at familiar occurrences afresh provokes insights and questions. Zeno's paradoxes have been extremely fruitful.

C. Zeno's paradoxes bring up questions about infinity and instantaneous motion.

IV. In this course, we emphasize the ideas of calculus more than the mechanical side.

A. But I must add that one of the reasons that calculus has been of such importance for these last 300 years is that it *can* be used in a mechanical way. It can be used by people who don't understand it. That's part of its power.

B. Perhaps we think calculus is hard because the word *calculus* comes from the Greek word for *stones* (stones were used for reckoning in ancient times).

C. Calculus does have a fearsome reputation for being very hard, and part of the goal of this course is to help you see calculus in a different light.

D. In describing his college entrance examinations in his autobiography, Sir Winston Churchill says, "Further dim chambers lighted by sullen, sulphurous fires were reputed to contain a dragon called the 'Differential Calculus.' But this monster was beyond the bounds appointed by the Civil Service Commissioners who regulated this stage of Pilgrim's heavy journey." We will attempt to douse the dragon's fearsome fires.

E. Another reason calculus is considered so forbidding is the size of calculus textbooks. To students, a calculus book has 1,200 different pages. But to a professor, it has two ideas and lots of examples, applications, and variations.

V. Fortunately, the two fundamental ideas of calculus, called the *derivative* and the *integral*, come from everyday observations.

A. Calculus does not require complicated notation or vocabulary. It can be understood in English.

B. We will describe and define simply and understandably those two fundamental ideas in Lectures Two and Three. Both ideas will come about from analyzing a car moving down a straight road and just thinking very clearly about that scenario.

C. The viewer is not expected to have any sense whatsoever of the meanings of these ideas now. In fact, I hope these technical terms inspire, if anything, only a foreboding sense of impending terror. That sense will make the discovery that these ideas are commonsensical and even joyful, instead of terrifying, all the sweeter.

D. The derivative deals with how fast things are changing (instantaneous change).

E. The integral provides a dynamic view of the static world, showing fixed objects growing by accretion (the accumulation of small pieces).

F. We can even view apparently static things dynamically. For example, we can view the area of a square or the volume of a cube dynamically by thinking of it as growing rather than just being at its final size.

G. The derivative and the integral are connected by the *Fundamental Theorem of Calculus*, which we will discuss in Lecture Four.

H. Both of the fundamental ideas of calculus arise from a straightforward discussion of a car driving down a road, but both are applicable in many other settings.

VI. The history of calculus spans two and a half millennia.

    A. Pythagoras invented the Pythagorean Theorem in the 6th century B.C., and as we know, Zeno posed his paradoxes of motion in the 5th century B.C.

    B. In the 4th century B.C., Eudoxus developed the Method of Exhaustion, similar to the integral, to study volumes of objects.

    C. In about 300 B.C., Euclid invented the axiomatic method of geometry.

    D. In 225 B.C., Archimedes used calculus-like methods to find areas and volumes of geometric objects.

    E. For many centuries, other mathematicians developed ideas that were important prerequisites for the full development of calculus.

        1. In around 1600, Johannes Kepler and Galileo Galilei worked making mathematical formulas that described planetary motion.

        2. In 1629, Pierre de Fermat developed methods for finding *maxima* of values, a precursor to the idea of the derivative.

        3. In the 1630s, Bonaventura Cavalieri developed the "Method of Indivisibles," and later, René Descartes established the Cartesian Coordinate System, a connection between algebra and geometry.

    F. The two mathematicians whose names are associated with the invention or discovery of calculus are Isaac Newton and Gottfried Wilhelm von Leibniz. They independently developed calculus in the 1660s and 1670s.

    G. From the time of the invention of calculus, other people contributed variations on the idea and developed applications of calculus in many areas of life.

1. Johann and Jakob Bernoulli were two of eight Bernoullis who were involved in developing calculus.
2. Leonhard Euler developed extensions of calculus, especially infinite series.
3. Joseph Louis Lagrange worked on calculus variations, and Pierre Simon de Laplace worked on partial differential equations and applied calculus to probability theory.
4. Jean Baptiste Joseph Fourier invented ways to approximate certain kinds of dependencies, and Augustin Louis Cauchy developed ideas about infinite series and tried to formalize the idea of *limit*.
5. In the 1800s, Georg Friedrich Bernhard Riemann developed the modern definition of the *integral*, one of the two ideas of calculus.
6. In the middle of the 1850s—about 185 years after Newton and Leibniz invented calculus—Karl Weierstrass formulated the rigorous definition of *limit* that we know today.

VII. Here is an overview of the lectures.

A. In Lectures Two, Three, and Four, we will introduce the basic ideas of calculus in the context of a moving car and discuss the connection between those ideas.

B. Then, we have a series of lectures describing the meaning of the derivative graphically, algebraically, and in many applications.

C. Following that, we have a similar series of lectures showing the integral from graphical, algebraic, and application points of view.

D. The last half of the course demonstrates the richness of these two ideas by showing examples of their extensions, variations, and applications.

E. The purpose of these lectures is to explain clearly the concepts of calculus and to convince the viewer that calculus can be understood from simple scenarios.
1. Calculus is so effective because it deals with change and motion and allows us to view our world as dynamic rather than static.
2. Calculus provides a tool for measuring change, whether it is change in position, change in temperature, change in demand, or change in population.

F. Calculus is intrinsically intriguing and beautiful, as well as important.

G. Calculus is a crowning intellectual achievement of humanity that all intelligent people can appreciate, understand, and enjoy.

Readings:

Cajori, Florian. "History of Zeno's Arguments on Motion," *The American Mathematical Monthly*, Vol. 22, Nos. 1–9 (1915).

Churchill, Winston Spencer. *My Early Life: A Roving Commission.*

Any standard calculus textbook.

Questions to Consider:

1. Find things or ideas in your world that you usually view as complete and fixed and think about them dynamically. That is, view their current state as the result of a growing or changing process.

2. Explore the idea of function by describing dependent relationships between varying quantities that you see in everyday life. For example, in what way is the amount of money in a savings account dependent on interest rate and time? Or, for a less quantitative example, how is happiness a function of intellectual stimulation, exercise, rest, and other variables?

3. Think of a scenario from your daily life that interests you. Keep it in mind as you progress through the lectures—can calculus be applied to understand and analyze it?

Lecture Two

Stop Sign Crime—
The First Idea of Calculus—The Derivative

Scope: Change is a fundamental feature of our world: temperature, pressure, the stock market, the population—all change. But the most basic example of change is motion—a change in position with respect to time. We will start with a simple example of motion as our vehicle for developing an effective way to analyze change. Specifically, suppose we run a stop sign, but in preparation for potential citations, we have a camera take a picture of our car neatly lined up with the stop sign at the exact instant that we were there. We show this photograph to the officer and ask to have the ticket dismissed, presenting the photograph as evidence. The officer responds by analyzing our motion in a persuasive way that illustrates the first of the two fundamental ideas of calculus—the *derivative*. We get the ticket but can take some solace in resolving one of Zeno's paradoxes.

Outline

I. Calculus has two fundamental ideas (called the *derivative* and the *integral*)—one centered on a method for analyzing change; the other, on a method of combining pieces to get the whole.

  A. Both of the fundamental concepts of calculus arise from analyzing simple situations, such as a car moving down a straight road.

  B. This lecture presents an everyday scenario that leads to one of the two ideas of calculus—the derivative.

II. The following stop-sign scenario is a modern-day enactment of one of Zeno's paradoxes of motion.

  A. Let us suppose we have a car driving on a road, and there is a mileage marker at every point along the road. Such a simple scenario can be represented in a graph.

  1. The horizontal axis is the time axis.

  2. The vertical axis tells us the position of the car at each moment of time.

  3. For the sake of arithmetic simplicity, we will talk about measuring the velocity (speed) of the car in miles per minute.

Therefore, the vertical axis of our graph is in miles and the horizontal axis is in minutes.

B. Suppose Zeno is driving this car, and he goes through a stop sign without slowing down.

C. Soon thereafter, he is pulled over by Officers Newton and Leibniz. (The corny names will make memorable how the roles in this drama relate to Zeno's paradox and the invention of calculus.)

D. The driver, Zeno, protests by showing a still picture of his car exactly at the stop sign at the exact moment, 1 minute after the hour, when he is supposed to have been running the stop sign. On this street, time is measured by stating the minutes only.

E. Zeno claims that there could be no violation because the car was in one place at that moment.

III. Officers Newton and Leibniz produce additional evidence.

A. The officers produce a still photo of the car at 2 minutes after the hour clearly showing the car 1 mile beyond the stop sign.

B. Zeno argues, "So what? At 1 minute, I was stopped at the stop sign."

C. Newton: "But you must admit your average velocity between 1 and 2 minutes was 1 mile per minute."

    1. To compute the average velocity during any interval of time, you need to know the position of the car at the beginning, the position at the end, and the amount of time that passed.

    2. The average velocity is change in position divided by change in time, that is, how far you went divided by how long it took.

    3. The average velocity does not rely on what happened between those two moments—just on where the car is at the beginning and at the end.

D. Again, Zeno says, "So what?"

E. Officers Newton and Leibniz produce an infinite amount of additional evidence, all incriminating. They note that Zeno was at the 1.1 mile marker at 1.1 minute, at the 1.01 mile marker at 1.01 minute, and so on, all of it proving that Zeno's velocity was 1 mile per minute.

IV. The idea of instantaneous velocity is the result of an infinite amount of data.

A. All the evidence is that, on every even incredibly tiny interval of time, the average velocity was 1 mile per minute.

B. The cumulative effect of all the evidence—an infinite number of intervals—leads to the idea of instantaneous velocity.

V. Knowing the position of a car at every moment allows us to compute the velocity at every moment. This can be illustrated with a car whose velocity is increasing.

   A. Let's now consider the example where at every time, measured in minutes and denoted by the letter t, we are at mileage marker t^2 miles. For example, at time 1, the car is at position 1, but at time 2, it is at position 4 (2^2), and at time 0.5, it is at position 0.25 (0.5^2).

   B. If we know where the car is at every time during an hour, we can tell how fast it was going at any selected moment by doing the infinite process of finding instantaneous velocity.

   C. Let's apply that infinite process to this moving car at several different times t.

   1. First, if time $t = 2$ minutes, the position of the car is $2^2 = 4$. Then, if time $t = 1$ minute, the position of the car is $1^2 = 1$. Subtracting 1 from 4 and dividing by 1 minute, we have 3 miles per minute. In other words, by looking at where the car was 1 minute after the 1-minute mark, we find that the average velocity was 3 miles per minute.

   2. However, when we look at shorter intervals of time, we get a different story, as shown in the chart below. We will find the positions of the car at various nearby times, such as 1.1, 1.01, 1.001, and 0.99 minutes, and compute our average velocity between time 1 and those times.

Position: $p(t) = t^2$		
Initial Time	**Final Time**	**Average Velocity (mi/min)**
1	2	3
1	1.1	2.1
1	1.01	2.01
1	1.001	2.001
0.999	1	1.999
Instantaneous velocity at $t = 1$ is 2 mi/min		

3. The whole collection of average velocities leads us to conclude that the instantaneous velocity is 2 miles per minute.

D. This process of taking smaller and smaller intervals of time to arrive at the instantaneous velocity is called a *limit*; the instantaneous velocity is the limit of the average velocities as the intervals of time get smaller and smaller.

E. The infinite process used to find the velocity at each time is the *derivative*. The derivative gives the instantaneous velocity at any given moment using this infinite process, if we know the position of the car at each moment.

F. If we look at the same question for other times, 0.7 minutes, for example, we have the following results:

Position: $p(t) = t^2$		
Initial Time	**Final Time**	**Average Velocity (mi/min)**
0.7	1.7	2.4
0.7	0.8	1.5
0.7	0.71	1.41
0.7	0.701	1.401
0.699	0.7	1.399
Instantaneous velocity at $t = 0.7$ is 1.4 mi/min		

G. If we look at the same question for other times, such as 1.4, 2, or 3 minutes, we have similar results for the instantaneous velocity.

H. We have been computing instantaneous velocities at various times for a car that is moving in such a manner that at every time t minutes, the car is at mileage marker t^2 miles. If we look at a chart of all our examples of instantaneous velocity, we see a pattern that indicates that at every time t, the velocity is $2t$ miles per minute.

Position: $p(t) = t^2$	
Time (min)	**Instantaneous Velocity (mi/min)**
0.7	1.4
1	2
1.4	2.8
2	4
3	6
Instantaneous velocity: $v(t) = 2t$	

VI. The first idea of calculus, the derivative, quantifies the idea of instantaneous velocity.

   A. We have taken a simple, everyday scenario (a moving car) and developed a simple, though infinite, process that made sense of the intuitive idea of motion or velocity at an instant.

   B. We now have an equation that tells us the instantaneous velocity at each moment of time.

   1. The derivative of a function $p(t)$ at time t is obtained by computing $\dfrac{p(t + \Delta t) - p(t)}{\Delta t}$, where Δt is a small increment of time, and then seeing what number those values approach as Δt becomes increasingly small.

   2. The single number to which those values approach is called the limit: $\dfrac{p(t + \Delta t) - p(t)}{\Delta t}$ as Δt approaches 0.

Readings:

Any standard calculus textbook, section introducing the derivative.

Questions to Consider:

1. Suppose a rocket is traveling along a road, and at each time t minutes its position is t^3 miles from where it started. Use the derivative process (and a calculator) to guess the instantaneous velocity of the rocket at various times, such as 1 minute, 2 minutes, and 3 minutes after starting.

2. Would it make sense to view position and time as discrete quantities having a little width to them? Then, a moving object could pause for an instant of time at one "point" before moving on. Zeno's fourth paradox of motion treats this situation when he considers three objects on parallel tracks, one moving right, one moving left, and one fixed. The relative velocities of these moving objects present a challenge. What is it?

Lecture Three

Another Car, Another Crime—
The Second Idea of Calculus—The Integral

Scope: The second idea of calculus helps us understand how to take
information about tiny parts of a problem and combine this
information to construct the whole answer. To develop this idea,
we return to the scenario of a moving car. In preparation, we take
our car out to a straight road, say to El Paso. We then videotape
only the speedometer as the car moves. We show some friends the
video of the speedometer and ask them to predict where we were
at the end of an hour. The process by which they use information
about velocity to compute the exact location of the car at the end
of the hour is the second of the ideas of calculus—the *integral*.

Outline

I.   In the last lecture, we introduced the derivative—the first of the two
basic ideas of calculus.

   A. The derivative allowed us to settle one of Zeno's paradoxes of
motion because it told us what we mean by the instantaneous
velocity of a moving car or arrow.

   B. Note that we did not fall into the trap of trying to divide 0 by 0 to
get the velocity at an instant.

II. The second fundamental idea of calculus arises from a scenario
involving another car and another crime.

   A. In this scenario, you are kidnapped, tied up in the back of the car,
and driven off on a straight road.

   B. You cannot see out of the car, but fortunately, you can see the
speedometer, and you have a video camera to take time-stamped
pictures of the speedometer. (There is no odometer in sight.)

   C. After 1 hour, you are dumped on the side of the road.

   D. How far have you gone?

III. What information can we extract from the videotape?

   A. Let's take a simple case: The car was going at a constant velocity.

1. At a constant velocity, computing how far we have gone in a given amount of time is easy. For example, if we go 1 mile per minute for 60 minutes, we will have gone 60 miles during that hour.

2. If we go 2 miles per minute for 20 minutes, we will have traveled 2 × 20, or 40 miles. On a graph, this constant velocity would appear as a horizontal line.

B. Let's take a harder case: Suppose our velocity changes. How do we compute the distance traveled?

C. Let's look at examples where our velocity is steady for some time, then abruptly changes to another velocity, and so on. Suppose we travel at:

1. 1 mile per minute between times 0 and 10 minutes,
2. 2 miles per minute for the time between 10 and 20 minutes,
3. 3 miles per minute for the time between 20 and 30 minutes,
4. 4 miles per minute for the time between 30 and 40 minutes,
5. 5 miles per minute for the time between 40 and 50 minutes, and
6. 6 miles per minute for the time between 50 and 60 minutes.

On a graph, this changing velocity would appear as "stair steps" going up.

D. Our total distance traveled will be:

$$(1 \times 10) + (2 \times 10) + (3 \times 10) + (4 \times 10) + (5 \times 10) + (6 \times 10)$$

miles; that is, 210 miles. (We were speeding.)

E. We now know the process of computing the total distance traveled if we know the velocity at each time and the velocities are steady at one velocity for a while, then jump to another velocity and so on throughout the whole hour.

IV. We know, however, that velocities do not jump like this and, instead, increase smoothly from one velocity to another. Dealing with variable velocities involves doing a little at a time and adding them up.

A. Our strategy is first to underestimate the distance traveled, then to overestimate the distance traveled, then to determine that the distance traveled is somewhere between these two.

B. Let's consider a car that is moving at each time t at velocity $2t$ miles per minute. That is, at 1 minute, we are traveling at a speed of 2 miles per minute; at 2 minutes, we are traveling at 4 miles per minute; and so forth. Because our car is going so fast, let's just see how far it goes during the first 3 minutes of travel.

C. In order to discover the distance covered, we will compare our car traveling smoothly at an increasingly higher velocity to a second car that is moving in the "jerky" or "jumpy" fashion we have seen above. We will also break the 3 minutes into smaller intervals of time, for example, half-minute intervals.

D. We then add up approximations of the distances traveled by the second "jerky" car during each short interval to approximate the total distance traveled.

    1. During each short interval of one-half minute, the car changed velocities.

    2. But if we assumed that the second "jerky" car continued at a steady velocity equal to the initial lower velocity during each little interval of time, we would get an *approximation* of the total distance traveled during that interval (7.5 miles).

    3. Because our car is always speeding up, the distance traveled by the second, "jerky" car will be an underestimate of the total distance our car traveled.

    4. Similarly, if we assumed that the second car went at a steady velocity equal to the fastest velocity our car actually went during each little interval of time, we would get an approximation to the total distance traveled during that 3-minute interval (10.5 miles).

    5. This approximation to the total distance traveled would be an overestimate.

    6. The correct answer would have to be somewhere between those two estimates.

E. The smaller the intervals, the more accurate will be the approximation to the distance traveled. Let's try breaking the time into intervals $1/10^{\text{th}}$ of a minute long.

    1. Once again, we can get an underestimate (8.7 miles) and an overestimate (9.3 miles).

    2. Notice that these over- and underestimates are closer to each other than before.

F. As the intervals get smaller, it doesn't matter what velocity we select from the range of velocities of the car in the intervals, because the car doesn't change velocity much in the tiny intervals.

G. Using increasingly smaller intervals produces increasingly better approximations.

V. The exact distance traveled can't be found with any single division of the interval of time.

    A. The exact answer is obtained by looking at infinitely many increasingly improved approximations.

    B. The finer approximations get closer and closer to a single value—the limit of the approximations.

    C. This infinite process is the second fundamental idea of calculus—the *integral*.

    D. If we know the velocity of a car at every moment in a given interval of time, the integral tells us how far the car traveled during that interval.

    E. Remember that the derivative was the limit of the average velocities as the intervals got smaller and smaller; likewise, the integral is the limit of the approximations as the intervals get smaller and smaller.

VI. We can use the same analysis to find out where we were at any moment.

    A. In the example above where the speedometer always reads $2t$, where are we after 1 minute, 2 minutes, 2.5 minutes, 3 minutes? In each case, we will use this infinite procedure to see how far we traveled from time 0 to these times.

    B. Let's look at the table and see if there is a pattern.

| Instantaneous velocity: $v(t) = 2t$ ||
Time (min)	Distance
0.5	0.25
1	1
1.5	2.25
2	4
3	9
Position: $p(t) = t^2$	

We can make a shrewd guess as to where we were after any time t: Namely, it appears that we are at the t^2 mileage marker.

C. Distance traveled is, thus, the square of the time interval taken, or $p(t) = t^2$.

D. The integral can be used to find the position of a moving car at each moment, if we know the velocity at each moment.

E. The integral process involves dividing the interval of time into small increments, seeing how far the car would have traveled if it had gone at a steady velocity during each small interval of time, and then adding up those distances to approximate the total distance traveled. Therefore, the formula to determine the distance traveled between time a and time b is:

$(v(a) \times \Delta t) + (v(a+\Delta t) \times \Delta t) + (v(a+2\Delta t) \times \Delta t) + \ldots$
$+ (v(b - \Delta t) \times \Delta t$, as Δt becomes increasingly smaller.

F. By taking smaller and smaller subdivisions and taking a limit, we arrive at the actual value of the integral.

Readings:

Any standard calculus textbook, the section introducing the definite integral.

Questions to Consider:

1. Suppose the speedometer on your rocket ship reads exactly $3t^2$ miles per minute at each time t minutes. Use the integral process to compute how far you will have traveled after 1 minute, 2 minutes, 3 minutes. Do you see an expression in t that gives the same answer?

2. Suppose your velocity is always $2t$ miles per minute at each time t minutes. How fine must your divisions of the interval of time be between time 0 and time 3 in order to be certain that your summation in the integral process is definitely within 1 mile of the correct answer?

Lecture Four

The Fundamental Theorem of Calculus

Scope: The *Fundamental Theorem of Calculus* makes the connection between the two processes discussed in the previous two lectures, the derivative and the integral. Again, this theorem can be deduced by examining the generative scenario of the moving car. The derivative and the integral involve somewhat complicated procedures that appear unrelated if viewed in the abstract; however, they accomplish opposite goals—one goes from position to velocity, the other goes from velocity to position. The duality between the derivative and integral is exactly what the Fundamental Theorem of Calculus captures. This convergence of ideas underscores the power of abstraction, one of the global themes of this series of lectures.

Outline

I. The two fundamental ideas of calculus, namely, the methods for (1) finding velocity from position (the derivative) and (2) finding distance traveled from velocity (the integral), involve common themes.

   A. Both involve infinite processes.

   B. Both processes involve examining a situation with increasingly finer time intervals.

   C. Both processes involve deducing a single answer from the whole infinite collection of increasingly accurate approximations.

II. We looked at the same situation—a car moving on a straight road—from two points of view.

   A. Knowing where we were at every moment, we deduced our velocity at every moment—the derivative.

   B. Knowing our velocity at every moment and where we started, we deduced where we were at every moment—the integral.

   C. The two processes are two sides of the same coin.

   D. Understanding implications of this relationship between these two processes is *the* fundamental insight of calculus. Indeed, it is known as the *Fundamental Theorem of Calculus*.

E. Specifically, suppose we are given a velocity function; that is, we are told how fast we are traveling at every instant between two times. We can find the distance traveled in a given time interval in two ways.

    1. First, we can compute the integral (by dividing the time interval into little pieces and adding up distance traveled over the little pieces).

    2. Second, if we know a position function whose derivative is the given velocity function, we can simply use the position function to tell us where we are at the end and where we were at the beginning, and then subtract the two locations to see how far we went.

F. Method 2 is a lot quicker. It does not involve an infinite number of approximations as the integral does.

G. These two ways of computing the distance traveled give the same answer. That's what makes the Fundamental Theorem of Calculus so insightful—it gives an alternative method for finding a value that would be hard or impossible or, at best, tedious to get, even with a computer.

III. The moving-car scenario presents a situation to analyze the Fundamental Theorem. Let's do so where the position function is $p(t) = t^2$, and the velocity function is $v(t) = 2t$.

A. We can find the distance traveled from time 1 to time 2 via the integral. Remember all the sums involved:

$(v(1) \times \Delta t) + (v(1+\Delta t) \times \Delta t) + (v(1+2\Delta t) \times \Delta t) + \ldots + (v(2 - \Delta t) \times \Delta t$, as Δt becomes increasingly smaller.

B. Then we can find the distance traveled knowing that $p(t) = t^2$ by subtraction. Because $p(2) = 4$ and $p(1) = 1$, the car traveled 3 miles.

C. We can consider other pairs of time values.

D. The summing process of the integral will always yield the same result as just subtracting the positions, because all these processes are referring to the same scenario of a moving car.

E. Suppose someone told us that the velocity of a car moving on a straight road at each moment t was $v(t) = 2t$ but didn't tell us the position function and asked for the distance traveled in the first 3 minutes. We could either add up pieces via the integral process or we could find the position function and subtract.

F. The fact that both processes yield the same answer is the importance of the Fundamental Theorem of Calculus.

G. The process of the integral (summing up pieces) tells us that the answer is what we want to know. That process refers directly to the commonsensical way of finding the distance traveled given the velocity.

H. If we can find a position function, it is much easier to just subtract.

IV. The fundamental insight relates the derivative and the integral.

A. The process of finding instantaneous velocity from position is the inverse of the process of finding position from velocity.

B. We have two ways that give the same answer to the question of how far we have gone given the velocity that we have been traveling.
1. One is by the infinite process of adding up (the integral).
2. One is by finding a function whose derivative is the velocity function (thus, it is a position function) and subtracting.
3. The insight is that both processes give the same result.

C. From an arithmetic point of view, the Fundamental Theorem notes that the process of subtraction and division that is at the heart of the derivative is the opposite of the process of multiplication and addition, which is at the heart of the integral.

D. This insight has many other applications, which we will see in future lectures.

V. The development of calculus was an incremental process, as we saw when we spoke of mathematicians before Newton and Leibniz.

A. Newton and Leibniz systematized taking derivatives and integrals and showed the connections between them.

B. The development of calculus, however, was involved in considerable controversy.

1. One type of controversy concerned who should get the credit for calculus, Newton or Leibniz.
2. The second type of controversy concerned the validity of the ideas underlying calculus, particularly the tricky business involved in
   taking limits. Let's take a few minutes to talk a bit about each of these controversies.

VI. Supporters of Newton and Leibniz had a lively and acrimonious controversy about who developed calculus first.

   A. Newton was quite averse to controversy, and this aversion made him reluctant to publish his work. Newton developed the ideas of calculus during the plague years of 1665–1666 when Cambridge was closed, but he did not publish those results for many years, in fact, not until 1704, 1711, and posthumously, in 1736. He did, however, circulate his ideas to friends and acquaintances in the 1660s.

   B. Leibniz was the first to publish his results on calculus. He conceived the ideas in 1674 and published them in 1684.

   C. In 1676, Newton learned that Leibniz had developed calculus-like ideas. Newton staked a claim on his priority in the invention of calculus by writing a letter to Leibniz.
      1. In this letter, Newton indicated his previous knowledge of calculus by writing an anagram.
      2. The anagram consisted of taking all the letters from the words of a Latin sentence, counting them, and putting all the letters in alphabetical order, as follows: "6a cc d æ 13e ff 7i 3l 9n 4o 4q rr 4s 9t 12v x."
      3. The sentence was, "*Data æquatione quotcunque fluentes quantitates involvente fluxiones invenire, et vice versa.*"
      4. This means, "Having any given equation involving never so many flowing quantities, to find the fluxions, and vice versa."
      5. Even the English version is not much of a hint of calculus.

   D. Some British supporters of Newton felt that Leibniz got the idea of calculus from Newton's manuscript during a visit that Leibniz made to England in 1674. Newton's supporters hinted at foul play in 1699.

E. Modern historians believe that Newton and Leibniz independently developed their ideas.

F. In any case, the controversy led to a downhill trend in relationships between the supporters of the two men.

G. The controversy had a bad effect on British mathematics for a long time.

VII. The other controversy associated with calculus involved its validity.

A. One thing that we have to understand is that, at the time of Leibniz and Newton, ideas that we consider absolutely fundamental to even starting to think about calculus today simply did not exist at all, for example, the idea of function.

B. Most vague, though, was the idea of the limit. Neither Leibniz nor Newton had firm ideas of the limit.

C. The concept of the limit was not resolved until the mid-1800s.

Readings:

Any standard calculus textbook, section on the Fundamental Theorem of Calculus.

Boyer, Carl B. *The History of the Calculus and Its Conceptual Development*.

Questions to Consider:

1. The derivative of the position function $p(t) = t^4$ yields a velocity function $v(t) = 4t^3$. Given that fact, use the Fundamental Theorem of Calculus to compute the distance a moving object will have traveled between time 0 and time 2 if its velocity at each time t is $4t^3$. If you like, you can check your answer by using the definition of the integral to compute the distance traveled.

2. We are here at one moment and there at another time. Thus, we know how far we traveled. Now let's look at this scenario dynamically, namely, how did we get there? Explain how the Fundamental Theorem of Calculus shows the connection between the dynamic and static views of the world.

Lecture Five
Visualizing the Derivative—Slopes

Scope: Motion and change underlie our appreciation of the world, both physically and in many other realms. Change is so fundamental to our vision of the world that we view it as the driving force in our understanding of most anything. Frequently, the dependency of one variable on another is most easily described visually by a graph, for example, a graph that shows position as a function of time. The concept of the derivative provides a method for analyzing change. We explore the relationship between the graph of a function and its derivative. For example, we observe that an upward-sloping graph signals a positive derivative. Superimposing the graph of the derivative on the graph of a function reveals a visual relationship between a function and its rate of change.

Outline

I. In this lecture, we will look at the derivative and its relation to graphs.

    A. Graphs show a relationship between two dependent quantities.

    B. For example, when referring to our moving car, our interest in the derivative is to try to understand how the change in time affects the change in the position of the car.

II. Change through time is of fundamental interest in many settings.

    A. Physical motion is change in position over time.

        1. Understanding such change over time is important.

        2. Cars moving, the idea of velocity, is a basic example.

    B. In biology, we can consider the change in human population in the world from 1900–2000, for example.

    C. In economics, we consider changes over time to prices, employment, production, consumption, and many other varying quantities. With a graph, we can show the changes in the Dow Jones Industrial Average over the last century.

    D. Understanding many important issues involves analyzing change in a characteristic over time. A graph can display the power output of the Chernobyl nuclear power plant on April 25–26, 1986. The steepness of the curve at 1:23 a.m. tells us how quickly the power output changed in a short amount of time, leading to the Chernobyl disaster.

E. These changes can be visualized using graphs.

III. Let's again analyze the velocity of a car given its position on a straight road.

 A. Let's look at the position graph and see how the velocity is related to the graph.

  1. First, looking at any position, we can figure out how fast the car is going.

  2. From the graph, we can deduce features about the motion of the car.

  3. If the graph is going up, the car is moving forward. If the graph is going down, the car is moving backward.

  4. The top or bottom of a graph means the car is momentarily stopped. Its velocity is 0.

  5. A steep graph corresponds to high velocity.

  6. A straight line means constant velocity—horizontal ↔ stopped; 45° upward to the right ↔ velocity of 1 mile per minute forward; 45° down to the right ↔ velocity of 1 mile per minute backward.

 B. Let's be more quantitative in our description.

  1. The steepness of the graph corresponds to the velocity. How exactly does it correspond?

  2. A straight-line position graph corresponds to a velocity equal to the slope of the line, where the slope is a quantitative measure of the steepness.

  3. Slope of a line is just the ratio of upward motion over sidewise motion, or the vertical change divided by the horizontal change.

   a. A straight line going upward to the right has a positive slope.

   b. A straight line going downward to the right has a negative slope.

   c. A horizontal line has slope 0.

IV. Consider now motion with varying velocities.

A. Recall the idea of the derivative and how that process gave the velocity. Let's see it with a curved graph of position for a car with varying velocities.

B. We look at nearby values and draw a straight line. The slope of that line is the change in position divided by the change in time.

C. As Δt becomes increasingly smaller, those straight lines converge to a tangent line whose steepness is telling us the instantaneous velocity.

D. Let's magnify the graph. Magnified, the graph looks more like a straight line, and the tangent line and the graph appear to coincide.

E. In general, the derivative at a point gives the slope of the line we would see if we magnified the graph.

F. Derivative, then, gives two equal quantities: (1) the velocity of the car and (2) the slope of the tangent line.

G. An important concept to remember is that smoothly curving lines, when viewed very close, look like straight lines. That is why the Earth looks flat to us even though we know it is curved.

V. We can see acceleration in the graph of a moving car.

A. Looking at examples of graphs, we can see where the velocity is increasing and decreasing.

B. We see that an upward-cupping graph corresponds to an accelerating car and a downward-cupping graph corresponds to a decelerating car.

C. Acceleration measures the change in the velocity over time.

D. Acceleration is itself a derivative—the derivative of velocity, or equivalently, the second derivative of position.

VI. In general, we observe the following relationships between functions and their derivatives:

A. A function is increasing if and only if its derivative is positive.

B. A function is decreasing if and only if its derivative is negative.

C. A function is "flat" if and only if its derivative is zero.

D. A function is concave up if its derivative is increasing, or equivalently, if its second derivative is positive. (This is the observation about acceleration we made earlier.)

E. A function is concave down if its derivative is decreasing, or equivalently, if its second derivative is negative. (This is the observation about deceleration we made earlier.)

F. Given a graph of a derivative, we can sketch the graph of the function, and likewise, given a graph of a function, we can sketch the graph of the derivative.

G. By sliding a tangent line along a graph and recording its slope at each point, we can generate the derivative graph.

VII. Let's look at the whole trip.

A. If you take a trip, you can easily compute what your average velocity was by taking the total distance between the starting and ending points and dividing by the time it took to cover that distance.

B. On a graph, that process is figuring out the slope of the line between the beginning and ending points.

C. Although your velocity may have varied during the trip, at some point, your instantaneous velocity will be exactly equal to your average velocity.

D. This reasonable observation is known as the *mean value theorem* (where *mean* means "average" rather than "cruel").

VIII. Let's summarize the relationship between a graph and the derivative.

A. The derivative of a graph at any point is equal to the slope of the tangent line.

B. If we magnify a smoothly curving graph, it will look like a straight line—the tangent line.

C. The perspective of a smooth curve looking like a straight line allows us to deduce various implications. One is known as *L'Hôpital's Rule*, after the man who wrote the first calculus textbook.

   1. L'Hôpital's Rule states that the limit of a ratio of two smooth functions, both of which approach 0, is equal to the limit of the ratio of their derivatives.

   2. A historical feature of L'Hôpital's Rule is that L'Hôpital did not discover it. He bought it from one of the Bernoulli brothers.

IX. When Newton and Leibniz defined the derivative in the 17th century, they used different words and different notation.

  A. Newton used a dot over a varying quantity to stand for the derivative. The problem with that notation is that an errant fly was capable of taking derivatives if it left its mark in the wrong place.

  B. Most people now use the notation for derivative that Leibniz introduced. Leibniz's notation includes the fundamental feature of the derivative as a quotient of changes, with Δ's becoming d's.

  1. For example, if $p(t) = t^2$, then

$$\frac{dp}{dt} = \frac{d}{dt}(t^2) = 2t.$$

  2. Often, y is a function of x, and the notation for derivative is $\frac{dy}{dx}$.

  3. This notation reminds us that the derivative arises from looking at ratios.

  4. The letter d reminds us of "difference," suggesting that the top value is, for example, a difference in the position of the moving car at two times, while the bottom is the difference in the time.

  C. If the function is presented as $p(t)$, then another notation for the derivative is $p'(t)$.

Readings:

Any standard calculus textbook, section introducing derivatives as slopes of tangent lines and section describing the connection between the graphs of functions and the graphs of their derivatives.

Questions to Consider:

1. When we look at a circle, we see a curve. Why is it that when we magnify a circle a great deal, it no longer looks curved?

2. Understand slopes of lines. That is, how does the slope measure the steepness of a line? Why is the slope of a line the same at each point of a line? Is the angle from the horizontal of a line doubled if the slope is doubled?

3. Draw a graph of a function—any function—and call it $p(t)$. Where is it increasing, decreasing, and constant? Where is it concave up or concave down? Can you sketch its derivative, $p'(t)$? Suppose what you drew first is actually $p'(t)$, can you sketch $p(t)$?

Lecture Six
Derivatives the Easy Way—Symbol Pushing

Scope: Much of the practical power of calculus lies in dealing with specific functions that model physical and conceptual situations. We now have a good conceptual sense of what the derivative means both physically and graphically. In this lecture, we'll see how to compute derivatives algebraically. Most functions that are used in physics, economics, geometry, or almost any area of study are expressions that involve basic arithmetic operations—addition, subtraction, multiplication, division—or exponents or trigonometric functions. Here, we see how these functions give rise to neat expressions for their derivatives and how these expressions agree with the geometric properties of the graphs we observed in the previous lecture. If we have an algebraic expression that tells us the position of a moving car, then we can deduce the algebraic expression for the velocity of the car at each moment without having to carry out the infinite process involved in taking derivatives at each point.

Outline

I.   In this lecture, we'll look at the derivative as it is manifested in algebra.

    A. Most functions used in almost any area of study are expressions that involve basic arithmetic operations.

    B. Here, we see how these functions give rise to expressions for their derivatives and how these expressions are obtained in a mechanical way.

    C. We will also see how these expressions agree with the geometric properties of the graphs we observed in Lecture Five.

II. Derivatives would be of no practical value if we had to do an infinite process at each point of time. Fortunately, we don't.

    A. The simplest function describing a moving car would occur when the car is moving at a steady velocity.

        1. In this case, the position function is $p(t) = ct$, where c is a constant.

2. The velocity, which is the same as the derivative, is just c.

3. Thus, if $p(t) = ct$, then $p'(t) = c$.

B. Let's look at a function we have already seen:

    1. $f(x) = x^2$ (which we have seen previously as $p(t) = t^2$).

Function	Derivative
x^2	$f'(x) = 2x$
0.7	1.4
1	2
1.4	2.8
2	4
3	6

    2. Notice in the table that for every number x, the derivative value was $2x$. How can we see in general that this is the case?

    3. We can check this derivative algebraically by considering the defining quotient for the derivative, namely,

$$\frac{f(x + \Delta x) - f(x)}{\Delta x} = \frac{(x + \Delta x)^2 - x^2}{\Delta x} = \frac{x^2 + 2x\Delta x + (\Delta x)^2 - x^2}{\Delta x}$$

$$= \frac{2x\Delta x + (\Delta x)^2}{\Delta x} = \frac{(2x + \Delta x)\Delta x}{\Delta x} = 2x + \Delta x.$$

    4. Now we take the limit as Δx gets smaller and smaller.

    5. Whether the function is $p(t) = t^2$ or $f(x) = x^2$, the answer is the same: $p'(t) = 2t$ or $f'(x) = 2x$.

C. Here are some related functions:

    1. If $f(x) = 5x^2$, then $f'(x) = 5(2x) = 10x$.

    2. More generally, if $f(x) = cx^2$, then $f'(x) = 2cx$.

D. Let's consider other functions of the form x^n.

    1. For the function $f(x) = x^3$, $f'(x) = 3x^2$.

    2. We can also understand this derivative algebraically by considering the defining quotient for the derivative, namely,

$$\frac{(x + \Delta x)^3 - x^3}{\Delta x}$$, and looking at the limit as Δx gets smaller and smaller.

3. We can see the pattern for finding the algebraic formula for the derivative of powers. If $f(x) = x^n$, then $f'(x) = nx^{n-1}$.

E. We see that if $h(x) = f(x) + g(x)$, then $h'(x) = f'(x) + g'(x)$.

1. Likewise, you can take one given function whose derivative you know and multiply it by a constant to get another function: For example, if $h(x) = cf(x)$, then $h'(x) = cf'(x)$.

2. This allows us to take derivatives of such functions as $5x^3 + 2x$.

   a. We see this as a sum of two different functions, $5x^3$ and $2x$, and we see each of those as a product of a constant times a function whose derivative we know. Therefore, if $h(x) = 5x^3 + 2x$, then $h'(x) = 15x^2 + 2$.

   b. And if we add a constant to the same function, for example, $h(x) = 5x^3 + 2x + 3$, then we still have $h'(x) = 15x^2 + 2$. Why? Because the derivative of a constant is 0, so it does not change the derivative.

F. Note that the derivative of a product is not simply the product of derivatives. The product rule and the quotient rule (if you have a function that is the quotient of two functions) are both rather more complicated algebraic equations.

G. At this stage, we can take the derivative of any polynomial, that is, a function of the form $a_n x^n + a_{n-1} x^{n-1} + \ldots + a_1 x + a_0$.

1. For example, let's take the function $f(x) = x^3 - 6x^2 + 9x + 1$. Note that the graph depicting this function starts down at the left, goes up, then down, and then goes up again.

2. The derivative of this function is $f'(x) = 3x^2 - 12x + 9$. Note that in the graph of this derivative, we see that it is the form of a parabola, going down and up again.

III. The derivative reduces the number of "bumps" in the graph of a function.

    A. A typical third-degree polynomial has a graph that goes up-down-up.

    B. Its derivative has a graph that goes down-up.

    C. A typical fourth-degree polynomial has a graph that goes down-up-down-up.

    D. Its derivative has a graph that goes up-down-up.

    E. We can see this geometrically by tracing the moving tangent line and recording the changing slopes.

    F. In looking at these examples, we see that the derivative has one less bump.

IV. Let's consider a function that is defined geometrically on a circle.

    A. If we take a right triangle whose angle is θ, the sine of the angle θ can be thought of as the ratio of the length of the side opposite θ divided by the length of the hypotenuse. The cosine of the angle θ is the ratio of the length of the side adjacent to θ divided by the length of the hypotenuse.

    B. On a circle of radius 1, the hypotenuse is 1; thus, sine of θ is just the vertical coordinate, and cosine of θ is the horizontal coordinate. That is, (cos θ, sin θ) are the coordinates of the point on the unit circle corresponding to the angle θ.

    C. As θ changes, so does the sin θ: When θ is small, so is sin θ; when θ approaches 90 degrees (or $\frac{\pi}{2}$ radians), sin θ approaches 1, and $\sin\left(\frac{\pi}{2}\right) = 1$.

D. Similarly, when θ is small, cos θ is close to 1; when θ approaches 90 degrees (or $\dfrac{\pi}{2}$ radians), cos θ approaches 0, and $\cos\left(\dfrac{\pi}{2}\right) = 0$.

E. Notice that the graphs of sine and cosine oscillate because their values repeat each time we move around the unit circle.

F. What is the derivative of sine? Look at the rate at which the line opposite the hypotenuse is changing in relation to a change in the angle.

G. The derivative of sine is cosine, and the derivative of cosine is negative sine.

H. We can graph these functions and see geometrically why their derivatives are related as they are. Neat.

V. An interesting question is this: Does there exist a function that is its own derivative at every point?

A. That is, is there a function $f(x)$, such that $f'(x) = f(x)$ at every x? Equivalently, we are looking for a function y that satisfies $\dfrac{dy}{dx} = y$.

B. It turns out that the *exponential function* $f(x) = e^x$, where $e = 2.718281828\ldots$, satisfies these conditions.

C. This leads us to the following table of derivatives:

Function	Derivative
$f(x)$	$f'(x)$
1	0
x	1
x^2	$2x$
x^3	$3x^2$
x^n	nx^{n-1}
$\sin x$	$\cos x$
$\cos x$	$-\sin x$
e^x	e^x

VI. If we are trying to find the answer to a question that involves derivatives, we will be able to solve it in a practical way.

  A. These equations help to mechanize the process of finding the derivative.

  B. If a law of nature, for example, involves derivatives, then we will often be able to express that law with a simple, computable formula.

  C. We will use this ability in the next lectures that show some applications of the derivative.

Readings:

Any standard calculus textbook, sections on differentiation formulas.

Questions to Consider:

1. Suppose $f'(2) = 3$ and $g'(2) = 4$. If $h(x) = f(x) + g(x)$ for every x, why is $h'(2) = 7$? This shows that the derivative of the sum is the sum of the derivatives. Warning: This pattern does not hold up for products.

2. Why do you believe that many aspects of nature and human creations are so well described by rather simple functions?

Lecture Seven
Abstracting the Derivative—Circles and Belts

Scope: The true power of the derivative lies in its ability not only to help us understand change with respect to time but also to deal with totally different types of dependent quantities. For example, the area of a circle is dependent on its radius; thus, we can describe the rate at which the area changes when the radius changes. In the previous lecture, we saw how the derivative behaves algebraically, so we can easily compute algebraically the derivative of the function that tells us the area of a circle of a given radius. Here, we show how to interpret the answer geometrically. That is, we see what the derivative means visually when we apply the concept of derivative to formulas for area and volume. Our geometric insight leads to a surprising realization about the roominess of belts around the Earth.

Outline

I. In this lecture, we continue our study of the derivative.

    A. In Lecture Five, we saw how the derivative is expressed graphically.

    B. In the last lecture, we saw how to express a derivative algebraically.

    C. In this lecture, we will see how to interpret a derivative geometrically.

II. The concept of the derivative can be generalized to apply to any two dependent quantities.

    A. The derivative can be applied to all cases of two interrelated quantities.

        1. The derivative describes how a change in one quantity entails a change in the other.

        2 For example, the area of a circle is dependent on its radius. We can discuss quantitatively the rate at which an increase in the radius of a circle would change the area of the circle.

B. The derivative measures the rate at which a change in a variable causes change in a dependent quantity.

III. We will now see that the algebraic formulas for derivatives developed in the previous lecture make perfect intuitive and geometrical sense in situations other than motion, as well.

A. We start with the square. The area of a square is $A(x) = x^2$, where x is its side length.

    1. Algebraically, we know that the derivative is $A'(x) = 2x$. That is, for every unit increase in the side length x, the area increases by roughly $2x$. But where does this come from?

    2. Let's see visually what the derivative means. That is, we want to compare the area of one square with the area of another square that is slightly bigger. Traditionally, we use the term Δx to measure the change in the length of the side.

    3. At a given side length, we can compute how much the area would increase if we increased the length of the side.

    4. The influence of a change in the length of the side varies depending on how big the square is to start with.

    5. Note the fraction we get when we look at the ratio of the change in area over the change in the length of the side:

$$\frac{(x + \Delta x)^2 - x^2}{\Delta x}$$

    6. We find the exact rate of change by taking the limit as Δx goes to zero and arriving at the derivative.

        a. For the larger square, we take the augmented rectangular area of one side, which is $x\Delta x$, and add it to the augmented area of the other side, $x\Delta x$, and finally, we add the area of the smaller square where the added lengths meet $(\Delta x)^2$.

        b. We then divide by Δx, so we have:

$$\frac{(x\Delta x + x\Delta x + (\Delta x)^2)}{\Delta x} = 2x + \Delta x.$$

  c. As Δx gets smaller and approaches 0, it becomes negligible, and essentially, we arrive at $2x$, exactly as predicted by the algebra.

B. Let's now consider the volume of a cube. The volume is $V(x) = x^3$, where x is its side length.

 1. Algebraically, we know that the derivative is $V'(x) = 3x^2$. That is, for every unit increase in the side length x, the volume increases by roughly $3x^2$. But where does this come from?

 2. As with the square, at a given side length, we can compute how much the volume would increase if we increased the length of the side.

 3. Let's look at how much volume we add if we increase the length by Δx on all three sides of the cube.

 4. The influence of a change in the length of the side varies depending on how big the cube is to start with. In any case, it adds a layer or "slab" of extra volume on three faces of the cube.

 5. The added volume for one side is $x^2 \Delta x$, where Δx indicates the added thickness. We do the same for all three sides and arrive at $3x^2 \Delta x$. To find the rate of growth, we divide by Δx and arrive at $3x^2$. We have four other tiny additional pieces of volume right at three edges of the cube and at one corner, but as Δx grows smaller and approaches 0, these tiny parts of the volume become increasingly negligible and tend to disappear, and we see the rate of growth is $3x^2$, exactly as predicted by the algebra.

C. Let's consider how the derivative would be defined in the case of the area of a circle viewed as dependent on its radius, $A(r) = \pi r^2$.

 1. Again, from the previous lecture, we know $A'(r) = 2\pi r$; that is, for every unit increase in the radius, the area increases by roughly 2π, or a little over 6 units. Why does this make sense?

2. At a given radius, we could compute how much the area would increase if the radius were increased a certain amount Δr.
3. The ratio of that change in area divided by the change in radius Δr would yield a rate of change of the area with respect to a change in the radius.
4. The additional area (called an *annulus*) is in the shape of a thin washer or ring or belt whose width is Δr and whose length is the circumference of the circle, $2\pi r$.
5. Thus, the additional area is approximately equal to the thickness of the ring times the length around the circle; that is, the additional area is about $2\pi r\Delta r$.
6. When we divide that change in the area by the thickness of the ring, Δr, we get a number that is approximately equal to the circumference of the circle, $2\pi r$.
7. This ratio of change of area divided by change in radius again approximates the influence of radius on area.
8. Thus, we obtain an intuitive understanding for $A'(r) = 2\pi r$.

IV. Suppose a belt is put around the equator of the Earth (about 25,000 miles). Suppose we increase the length of the belt by 7 feet so that it hovers above the Earth. How far away from the Earth will it be?

A. The circumference of a circle of radius r is $2\pi r$.

B. From the previous lecture, we know that the derivative is 2π. This means that every unit increase in r results in roughly 2π (or just over 6) units increase in the circumference.

C. Most people guess wrong about the belted Earth, assuming that the longer belt will hover just slightly off the ground.
1. In fact, the derivative tells us that adding 7 feet to the circumference of the belt will result in the belt being more than a foot away from the Earth!
2. In other words, we have added more than a foot to the radius of the belt. We can understand this result better if we look at the derivative, 2π.
3. A 1-foot change in the radius of the belt brings about roughly an addition of 6.28 feet to the length of the circumference of

the belt. Therefore, adding 7 feet to the length of the belt would indeed result in the belt being more than a foot away from the Earth.

V. Now let's consider a stalactite growing in a cave. How quick does a 20,000-year-old stalactite acquire volume compared to its 10,000-year-old cousin?

    A. Depending on the environment, stalactites usually grow in cone-like shapes at the rate of 1–4 inches every 1,000 years. We'll assume our stalactites grow at the rate of 3 inches every 1,000 years.

    B. We'll also assume that the ratio of the stalactite's base radius to its height is 1:6.

    C. If a stalactite is x thousand years old, its height is $3x$ inches and its radius is $\dfrac{x}{2}$ inches. Therefore, at 10,000 years, the stalactite is 30 inches high and has a radius of 5 inches; at 20,000 years, the stalactite is 60 inches high and has a radius of 10 inches.

    D. The volume or weight of the stalactite when it is x thousand years old is $W(x) = \dfrac{1}{3}$ base times height, or

$$W(x) = \frac{1}{3} \pi \left(\frac{x}{2}\right)^2 3x = \frac{\pi x^3}{4}.$$

    E. What is the growth rate of the weight of the stalactite? It is precisely the derivative of the weight.

    F. Using our table of derivatives, we see that $W'(x) = \dfrac{3\pi x^2}{4}$.

Therefore, the derivative of the weight at 10,000 years is 75π, while at the 20,000-year mark, it is 300π.

    G. Thus, even though the 20,000-year-old and the 10,000-year-old stalactites increase in *height* at the same rate, the older one increases in weight at 4 times the rate of the younger one!

VI. Let's consider how we would define the derivative for dependencies involving supply and demand.

    A. We see that the supply curve shows how many items producers would produce if the price they could sell the item at were p. The demand curve shows how many items consumers would buy if the price were p.

    B. In this graphical representation of the curves, notice that if the price increases, the supply increases.

    C. Also notice that if the price increases, the demand decreases.

    D. The place where the demand curve and the supply curve cross is the point where we expect the price to be.

    E. What does the derivative measure, when applied to the supply and demand curves?

    F. If the curves are steep near the crossing point, slight increases in price would cause major increases in supply and major decreases in demand. These are elastic goods.

    G. Goods that are insensitive to price, for example, gasoline, are called inelastic.

VII. We have now seen the importance of the derivative.

    A. The derivative analyzes change.

    B. The derivative gives a quantitative view of how one quantity will change when another quantity on which it is dependent changes.

    C. Analyzing dependencies and change is one of the most fundamental things we do to try to understand our world.

    D. The derivative in general arose from first analyzing the simple case of a moving car. That example illustrated one example of dependency—position was dependent on the time.

    E. We then saw that the same analysis would serve in many cases where one quantity is dependent on another.

Readings:

Any standard calculus textbook, sections on applications and interpretation of derivatives. (These explanations may be difficult to find in standard texts.)

Questions to Consider:

1. Consider an animal whose weight varies according to height according to the function $w(h) = h^3$. Suppose the strength of the animal's legs at a given height is given by $s(h) = h^2$. Could similar animals exist that are 10 times as tall? Does this help explain the limit to the size of land animals?

2. Suppose the population increases by 1% each year. Does the derivative of the population function (that is, the function whose value is the population at each time) increase, decrease, or stay the same over time?

Lecture Eight
Circles, Pyramids, Cones, and Spheres

Scope: How do we find formulas for the areas of objects, such as circles, and the volumes of solids, such as cones, pyramids, and spheres? We can deduce each of these formulas by dividing the object into small pieces and seeing how the small pieces can be assembled to produce the whole. The area of a circle, πr^2, is a wonderful example of a formula that we may just remember with no real sense of why it's true. But we can view the circle in a way that shows clearly whence the formula arises. The process involves a neat method of breaking the circle into pieces and reassembling those pieces. This example and others illustrate techniques of computing areas and volumes that were ancient precursors to the modern idea of the integral.

Outline

I. Greek mathematicians had a keen sense of integral-like processes. We look first at an ancient process for discovering the formula for the area of a circle.

   A. Remember that the number π is the ratio of the circumference of a circle to its diameter.

   B. A circle of radius r can be broken into small wedges.

   C. The wedges can be assembled by alternately putting one up and one down to create a shape almost like a rectangle.

   D. As the wedges are made ever tinier, the assembled shape more and more closely approximates a rectangle.

   E. The top plus the bottom of the rectangle is precisely the circumference of the circle, therefore, of total length $2\pi r$.

   F. Thus, the top is πr long.

   G. The height of the rectangle is ever closer to r.

   H. The rectangle is approaching a rectangle of height r and width πr; hence, it has area $r\pi r$ or πr^2, the familiar formula for the area of a circle.

II. The derivative gives a dynamic view of the relationship between the area of a circle and its radius.

   A. We find that the derivative of the area (the change in area divided by change in radius) must equal the circumference of the circle.

   B. When we add thin bands to a circle to increase its size, then divide by the increment that we made to the radius, that division gives us the length of the circumference.

   C. Therefore, the derivative of πr^2 equals $2\pi r$. The derivative measures how fast the area of the circle is changing relative to a change in the radius.

III. The area of a triangle is dependent only on the height and base, not on whether or how much it is leaning.

   A. The area of a right triangle is easy to calculate because it is half of a rectangle.

   B. We can see that the area of any triangle depends only on its base and height by sliding thin pieces to the side to create a right triangle.

   C. Therefore, we find that the area of any triangle is equal to $\dfrac{1}{2}$ the base times the height.

   D. In fact, we can use this formula to calculate the area of a circle by imagining the circle divided into tiny triangles.

      1. All the triangles have the same height (r), and the sum of the bases of all triangles equals the circumference of the circle $(2\pi r)$.

      2. Therefore, the sum of the area of all the triangles equals the total of the bases $(2\pi r)$ times the height (r) divided by 2, or πr^2, again, the familiar formula for the area of a circle.

IV. We can determine the volume of a tetrahedron (a pyramid over a triangular base) by thinking of sliding its parts as we did with the triangle.

   A. The volume of a tetrahedron is determined only by the area of the base and its height, regardless of where the top point of the tetrahedron lies.

B. It is difficult to compute the volume of a tetrahedron, so we start with the volume of a prism.

C. The area of a prism is the area of its base times the height. Three tetrahedra of the same volume fill up a prism; thus, the volume of a tetrahedron is $\frac{1}{3}$ the area of its base times its height.

D. Once we know the volume of a tetrahedron, we can determine the volume of a pyramid.

    1. A pyramid can be seen as two tetrahedra if its square base is divided into two triangles.

    2. The volume of the pyramid, therefore, is equal to $\frac{1}{3}$ the area of half of its base times its height plus $\frac{1}{3}$ the area of half of its base times its height. In other words, the volume of a pyramid equals $\frac{1}{3}$ the area of the base times the height.

V. The volume of a cone is easy to compute once we know the volume of a tetrahedron.

    A. A cone can be approximately filled up by tetrahedra each with the same point as the cone point and with the bases of the tetrahedra on the base of the cone.

    B. Given that the volume of each tetrahedron is $\frac{1}{3}$ the area of its base times its height and the height is the same as the height of the cone, then the volume of the cone is also $\frac{1}{3}$ the area of the base of the cone times its height.

VI. The surface area of a sphere can be computed by breaking that surface into small pieces.

    A. The area between latitude lines on a sphere is the same as the area of a band around the surrounding cylinder if the band is contained between parallel planes that intersect the sphere on the two latitude lines. The smaller radii for latitudes near the North Pole are accompanied by the "slantiness" at those higher latitudes in such a way that the area on the sphere between parallel planes near the North Pole exactly equals the area on the sphere between parallel planes of the same fixed distance apart near the equator.

B. We can see that this area equality holds by looking at a picture of a circle and finding two similar right triangles that tell the story.

C. Thus, the surface area of the sphere is exactly the same as the area of the surrounding cylinder, or $4\pi r^2$.

VII. These examples show ancient ideas that resemble the modern idea of the integral. The ancients did not have a well-defined idea of what happens at the limit, but their arguments are persuasive and can now be made mathematically rigorous.

Readings:

Boyer, Carl B. *The History of the Calculus and Its Conceptual Development*.

Dunham, William. *Journey through Genius: The Great Theorems of Mathematics*.

Questions to Consider:

1. In thinking about the surface area of the sphere, why couldn't we approximate the area of the northern hemisphere by just thinking of triangular wedges going from the North Pole down to the equator and viewing each wedge as a triangle?

2. Is there a philosophical reason that the formulas for areas and volumes are so relatively simple? In other words, could you imagine a geometric world in which the area of circle or the surface area of a sphere was not so simple? There is a whole different world of ideas associated with non-Euclidean geometries in which such formulas are not as simple.

Lecture Nine
Archimedes and the Tractrix

Scope: In the 17th century, Bonaventura Cavalieri analyzed shapes and found formulas for the areas and volumes of geometrical figures using his *method of indivisibles*. Previously, in the 3rd century B.C., Archimedes devised an ingenious method using levers to deduce the formula for the volume of a sphere. The method foreshadowed the idea of the integral in that it involved slicing the sphere into thin sections. The idea of the integral provides effective techniques for computing volumes of solids and areas of surfaces. Then we move to the 21st century and a new method for computing areas developed by mathematician Mamikon Mnatsakanian.

Outline

I. In the 17th century, Bonaventura Cavalieri analyzed shapes using his *method of indivisibles*.

   A. If one thinks of the surface of a sphere as comprised of many tiny triangles, then the volume of the sphere can be viewed as made up of many tiny tetrahedra with those triangles as bases and the center of the sphere as the top of each tetrahedron.

   B. Because we know that the volume of each tetrahedron is $\frac{1}{3}$ the area of the base times the height, then the volume of the sphere will be $\frac{1}{3}$ the surface area of the sphere times the radius (the height of each tetrahedron).

   C. Because the surface area of the sphere is $4\pi r^2$, as we saw in the last lecture, the volume of the sphere is $\frac{1}{3}$ of the product of that area times the height of each tetrahedron, which is r, thereby giving the formula for the volume of the sphere, namely, $\frac{4}{3}\pi r^3$.

II. Archimedes had an amazing way to discover the formula for the volume of a sphere of radius r.

A. His method involved a lever.

B. He balanced a cone (with a base of radius $2r$ and a height of $2r$) and a sphere (of radius r) on one side of the lever with a cylinder (with a radius of $2r$ and a height of $2r$) on the other.

C. Archimedes's method for showing that the objects balance involved dividing the sphere, the cone, and the cylinder into thin slices and hanging those slices on the lever.

    1. Originally, one could picture the cylinder being in its horizontal position with the cone and sphere neatly inside it.

    2. Archimedes's insight was that if we take a thin slice through the cylinder (thereby cutting through the sphere and cone also), that thin slice of the cylinder (by itself, left where it is, at point x distance from the fulcrum) would be exactly counterbalanced if the slices of the cone and sphere were both moved to the other side of the lever at distance $2r$ from the fulcrum.

    3. Because that insight is true for each slice, the totality of all the slices all the way along the cylinder shows that the cylinder, cone, and sphere will balance on the lever as described above.

D. In our demonstration, we can see that placing the sphere and cone exactly $2r$ from the fulcrum balances the cylinder.

    1. The cylinder lies horizontally along the lever with one end at the fulcrum and the other at $2r$.

    2. Both the cone and the sphere are hung from the same point on the other side of the lever, namely, at the point that is distance $2r$ from the fulcrum.

    3. If we know that the cone, sphere, and cylinder balance, and we know the volumes of all the objects except the sphere, then we can deduce the volume of the sphere.

E. Thus, Archimedes found that a sphere of radius r has a volume of $\dfrac{4}{3}\pi r^3$.

F. Today, we would formalize this procedure of slicing up a sphere by using integrals.

III. Let's examine the relationship between the surface area of a sphere and its volume.

    A. Knowing the meaning of the derivative, we know that the derivative of the volume is telling us the rate at which the volume is changing relative to a change in the radius.

    B. Geometrically, that rate of change is the volume of a thin layer over the surface of the sphere divided by the thickness. As the thickness gets tiny, that fraction will simply equal the surface area.

    C. Using our knowledge of derivatives, we know algebraically that the derivative of $\dfrac{4}{3}\pi r^3$ is $4\pi r^2$, which is the formula for the surface area of a sphere.

    D. The derivative of the volume of the sphere must give a formula for the surface area of the sphere—and we see it does.

IV. In the 21st century, Mamikon Mnatsakanian devised an ingenious method for computing areas by breaking up regions into pieces that are sectors of a circle.

    A. The area between two concentric circles can be computed in two ways.

        1. Just subtracting the area of the smaller circle from the area of the larger circle is one method to arrive at the area of the ring (annulus).

        2. The Mnatsakanian method is to view the annulus as a polygon with many, many sides.

            a. We can sweep and shift the small triangular segments that make up the annulus and see that the sum of those segments will be the area of a circle.

            b. We find that the area of the annulus is πa^2, where a is the distance from a tangent point on the small circle to the outer circle.

    B. This method also provides a proof of the Pythagorean Theorem.

    C. This method can be used when computing the area under a tractrix.

        1. A *tractrix* is a curve created by pulling one end of a string along the *x*-axis while the other end, attached to a pen, starts on the *y*-axis and is dragged along to create the curve.

2. One way to compute the area under the tractrix is to view that area as a sweeping of tangent lines and to approximate the area as segments of a circle. The method shows that the area is simply equal to a quarter of a circle $\left(\dfrac{1}{4} \pi a^2 \right)$.

3. The hard way to compute the area under the curve involves finding the formula for a tractrix.

V. Both Archimedes's and Mnatsakanian's methods involve breaking up an object into small pieces and adding up their contributions. This strategy is the fundamental strategy of the integral.

Readings:

Boyer, Carl B. *The History of the Calculus and Its Conceptual Development*.

Dunham, William. *Journey through Genius: The Great Theorems of Mathematics*.

Mnatsakanian, Mamikon. *Visual Calculus by Mamikon*. www.its.caltech.edu/~mamikon/calculus.html.

Questions to Consider:

1. Experiment with a level to see that the formula for balancing on a lever is correct. See how putting two weights on one side is equivalent to putting one weight at a different location. What location?

2. Deduce the formula for the area of a circle using Cavalieri's method of indivisibles.

Lecture Ten
The Integral and the Fundamental Theorem

Scope: If a car goes at a constant velocity of 30 miles per hour, it is a simple matter to compute how far the car has traveled during an interval of time. We saw that to deal with varying velocity, we just break the total time into small intervals and add up approximations of how far the car traveled in each small interval of time. In this lecture, we will see the geometric implications of this integral process as we view it in graphical form. In particular, we see that the same process that computes the distance traveled by the car also computes the area between the graph of the velocity curve and the axis. We use Leibniz's notation for the integral because the long S shape reminds us that the definition of the integral involves sums.

Outline

I. After our introduction to the precursors to the modern concept of the integral, we will start a series of lectures that correspond to previous lectures about the derivative.

    A. We will see, first, the integral in its graphical interpretation.

    B. We will then study the integral in its algebraic interpretation.

II. Recall how the integral was defined in the case of the car moving down a straight road.

    A. We are given the velocity function $v(t)$ and want to compute the total distance traveled.

    B. For example, if we know the car was traveling a constant 2 miles per minute for 3 minutes, we know the car traveled a total distance of 6 miles.

III. Let's look graphically at the scenario of a forward-moving car.

    A. Notice that the process of finding the distance traveled involves finding products that are equal to the areas of rectangles.

    B. That is, the distance is equal to the product of the height of the rectangle (the line representing a constant 2 miles per minute) times the width of the rectangle (the 3-minute mark on the horizontal axis) of the graph.

IV. Let's look at another velocity function in which velocity is two times the time, or $2t$, so we know the car will be traveling along at an ever-increasing velocity.

    A. Our graph in this case shows an upwardly sloping line. To compute the distance traveled, we break the interval of time into small bits and do some adding.

    B. We then approximate the velocity traveled within those small intervals of time (half-minute intervals) by assuming our car remained at a constant velocity during that time, then "jumped" to the next constant velocity at the next interval and so forth.

    C. We then add the distance for the first interval of time plus the distance for the second interval of time and so forth.

    D. Notice again that the process of finding the distance traveled involves finding products that are equal to the areas of rectangles.

    E. As the little intervals get smaller, the total of the area of the thin rectangles is getting ever closer to the area between the curve and the axis; that is, the approximations improve.

    F. This infinite process of taking ever-smaller intervals of time provides us with a single exact answer.

V. Let us add here that the notation for the integral is Leibniz's, namely, $\int_a^b v(t)dt$.

    A. The long S shape reminds us that the meaning of the integral involves *sums*.

    B. The a and b denote the starting and ending times, respectively.

    C. In the limit, the answer is exactly equal to the area under the curve.

    D. Thus, in integral notation form, $\int_a^b v(t)dt$, which we know is the distance traveled by the moving car, is also equal to the area under the graph of $v(t)$.

VI. Let's look at the specific example where the velocity at each moment is $2t$.

A. Then, $\int_0^3 2t\,dt$ is equal to the distance the car traveled between time 0 and time 3.

B. But $\int_0^3 2t\,dt$ is also equal to the area under the graph of $2t$.

C. We can check that area geometrically because the area under $2t$ between $t = 0$ and $t = 3$ is just a triangle with base 3 and height 6.

D. Thus, the car traveled $\dfrac{1}{2}(6 \times 3) = 9$ miles.

E. And the area under the graph of $2t$ from 0 to 3 is 9 square units.

VII. We can think about the motion of the car to see some features of the integral.

    A. The integral from a to b plus the integral from b to c equals the integral from a to c.

    B. This is obvious because it simply says that we see how far we went during the time a to b and how far we went from time b to c; the total is how far we went from time a to time c.

    C. Suppose the velocity is negative.
        1. When the velocity is negative, we are traveling backward.
        2. Then, the integral is telling how far backward we traveled.

    D. More exactly, the integral of the velocity is telling us not how far we drove, but how far we end up from where we started.

    E. Examples of when we are going forward part of the time and backward part of the time illustrate this concept.

VIII. Let's look at the graphical interpretation of integrals again.

    A. If the function is below the axis, then the integral is negative.

    B. If the function is part above the axis and part below, the integral combines the two.

    C. The definition of the integral just adds up the products, not of the height of the rectangles, but the signed height—positive if the function is positive and negative if the function is negative.

    D. It's easy. When the graph goes below the axis, the integral is negative; when above, positive.

E. The summation fact, a to b plus b to c equals a to c, works regardless of whether the graph goes above or below the axis.

IX. Integrals behave "opposite" of derivatives graphically.

A. For a function $f(x)$, we can define a function $F(x)$ as the integral of f from starting time a to ending time x. Think of f as the velocity and F as the mileage marker.

B. Recall that if a function $f(x)$ is increasing, then its derivative $f'(x)$ is positive, and if a function $f(x)$ is decreasing, then its derivative $f'(x)$ is negative.

C. For the integral, it's the opposite: If the function $f(x)$ is positive, then its integral $F(x)$ is increasing; if the function $f(x)$ is negative, then its integral $F(x)$ is decreasing.

D. If the function $f(x)$ is zero, then its integral $F(x)$ is constant—it's just $F(a)$ because we are not adding any area.

E. In summary, notice that we have $F'(x) = f(x)$.

X. Now let's turn to an algebraic representation of this same idea.

A. Given the equation for the velocity of a body, we can deduce the equation for its position using the integral.

B. The integral of the velocity is the position.

    1. Let's look at an example where we know the answer.

    2. Suppose $v(t) = 2t$. We do some calculating and see that the distance traveled is the height times the width divided by 2, or t^2.

    3. If we stop at any time, the integral will give an answer.

    4. The answer is always t^2.

XI. Recall that the Fundamental Theorem of Calculus relates the integral and the derivative.

A. If $v(t)$ is the velocity at every moment of a car moving down a straight road, then the integral of $v(t)$ between one time and another equals the net distance traveled.

B. Thus, $\int_a^b v(t)dt$ equals the net distance traveled between time a and time b.

C. We saw before that if we can find a position function $p(t)$ whose derivative is $v(t)$, then the integral is easy to compute.

    1. It is simply the position at time b minus the position at time a.

    2. If $p'(t) = v(t)$, then $\int_a^b v(t)dt = p(b) - p(a)$.

D. Whether the variable is t or any other letter, the relationship is the same.

E. Thus, the Fundamental Theorem of Calculus states:
$$\int_a^b F'(x)dx = F(b) - F(a).$$

F. Suppose we want to do the integral process (which involves doing infinitely many approximations, each of which is a sum) for some function $f(x)$. If we can find an *antiderivative* $G(x)$ for $f(x)$ (that is, a function such that $G'(x) = f(x)$), then we can get the answer to the integral process just by doing one subtraction, $G(b) - G(a)$. An *antiderivative* is a function whose derivative is the function whose integral we are trying to take.

G. When we are faced with an integral, our first thought is, "Can we find an antiderivative for the function that is under the integral sign?"

XII. Let's look at some examples.

A. Every derivative formula leads to an antiderivative formula, because we can just go backward.

B. For example, we know that the derivative of x^2 is $2x$. Thus, an antiderivative of $2x$ is x^2.

C. The derivative of a constant times x, $f(x) = cx$, is just c. That is, $f'(x) = c$, or $\dfrac{d}{dx}(cx) = c$. Thus, an antiderivative of the constant function c is just cx.

D. The derivative of $\dfrac{x^{n+1}}{n+1}$ is x^n. Thus, an antiderivative of x^n is $\dfrac{x^{n+1}}{n+1}$.

XIII. Why do we say *an* antiderivative rather than *the* antiderivative?

    A. Any two functions that differ by a constant value will automatically have the same derivative at each point.

    B. We can see this fact graphically.

        1. If two functions differ by a constant, then their graphs are merely shifted up and down.

        2. The slope of the tangent line above each point will be precisely the same.

        3. The derivative is just measuring the slope of the tangent line.

    C. For each function, instead of just one antiderivative, we really find one antiderivative, then add any constant to indicate that any shifting of the antiderivative is also an antiderivative of the same function.

    D. Just as we saw the table of derivatives in Lecture Six, now we have the table of antiderivatives.

Function	Antiderivative
$f(x)$	$F(x)$
x	$\dfrac{x^2}{2} + C$
x^2	$\dfrac{x^3}{3} + C$
x^3	$\dfrac{x^4}{4} + C$
x^n	$\dfrac{x^{n+1}}{n+1} + C$
$\sin x$	$-\cos x + C$
$\cos x$	$\sin x + C$
e^x	$e^x + C$

XIV. The most important thing to remember about integrals is what they mean.

    A. The integral is a number that is the result of doing an infinite process.

    B. The process involves approximating the answer.

    C. Each approximation is obtained by taking a sum.

    D. As we divide the interval up into smaller subintervals, the approximation gets better.

    E. For positive functions, the value of the integral is equal to the area under the curve and above the axis.

Readings:

Any standard calculus textbook, section defining the definite integral and exploring its properties.

Questions to Consider:

1. The integral is defined in terms of sums of products. One number in the product is the value of the function in a small interval. Why does it not matter which point in the interval you choose in defining the integral?

2. Explain why an integral that gives the volume of a solid is somehow adding up pieces of area that have no volume and combining them to create volume. That almost paradoxical perspective was an obstacle to understanding the integral for many years.

3. Use the Fundamental Theorem of Calculus to evaluate $\int_1^2 x^3 \, dx$.

Lecture Eleven
Abstracting the Integral—Pyramids and Dams

Scope: We saw the power of the derivative in its applications beyond motion: the dynamic view of areas and volumes, the growth of stalactites in caves, and supply and demand curves in economics. Similarly, the integral, when viewed abstractly, is an important tool for understanding diverse dynamical situations such as (again) areas and volumes, as well as engineering. In this lecture, we work out the volume of a pyramid, the volume of a cone, and a solution to an engineering problem: the hydrostatic pressure on a dam.

Outline

I.   In this lecture, we will see how the integral can be applied to questions that go beyond a car going on a straight road.

II. Areas and volumes are natural applications of the integral.

   A. Consider a square with side length x and area $A(x) = x^2$.

   1. When we studied the derivative, we saw that $A'(x) = 2x$ essentially represents the change in the area when we increase the side length by 1.

   2. This means that for each Δx increase in the side length, the area increases by approximately $2x\Delta x$.

   3. Thus, the total area of a square of side length 5 is the sum of all pieces for each Δx between 0 and 5, and it can be realized as an integral and evaluated by the Fundamental Theorem of Calculus: $A(5) = \int_0^5 2x\,dx = 5^2 - 0^2 = 25$

   B. Now consider a cube with side length x and volume $V(x) = x^3$.

   1. When we studied the derivative, we saw that $V'(x) = 3x^2$ essentially represents the change in the volume when we increase the side length by 1, remembering that adding to the length of the side adds a layer of extra volume on three faces of the cube.

2. Thus, again, for each Δx increase in the side length, the volume increases by approximately $3x^2\Delta x$.

3. The total volume of a cube of side length 5 is simply the integral of this function: $V(5) = \int_0^5 3x^2\,dx$

4. We can compute the integral using the Fundamental Theorem of Calculus. Because an antiderivative of $3x^2$ is x^3, we simply evaluate x^3 at the upper limit of integration and subtract x^3 evaluated at the lower limit of integration:

$$V(5) = \int_0^5 3x^2\,dx = 5^3 - 0^3 = 125$$

III. Now, let us look at more complicated examples, such as computing the volume of a pyramid with a square base of side length 200 ft and a height of 200 ft.

A. We can approximate the pyramid by a stack of slightly thickened squares placed on top of one another, in which the squares get smaller as we get near the top of the pyramid.

B. The volume of each thickened square is easy to write down, namely, it is the area of the square times the thickness.

C. The area of a square h units from the top is h^2, so the volume of each slice is approximately $h^2\Delta h$.

D. Adding up the volumes of those thickened squares gives an approximation to the volume of the pyramid. Thus, the total volume of the pyramid is $\int_0^{200} h^2\,dh.$

E. To evaluate the integral, we use the Fundamental Theorem of Calculus. An antiderivative of h^2 is $\dfrac{h^3}{3}$, so

$$\int_0^{200} h^2\,dh = \frac{200^3}{3} - \frac{0^3}{3} = \frac{200^3}{3} = 2{,}666{,}666\text{ft}^3$$

IV. Let's compute the volume of a cone of base radius 3 and height 4.

A. We can view the sideways cone as skewered on the *x*-axis, and we can think of slicing it up into thin slices as we would do to a loaf of bread.

B. Each slice is approximately the same volume as a slightly thickened disk, and the total volume of the cone is approximately equal to the sum of the volumes of those small slices.

C. Using similar triangles, we can see that at point *x*, the radius of the disk is $\dfrac{3x^3}{4}$, so the area of the disk is $\pi\left(\dfrac{3x}{4}\right)^2$, or $\dfrac{9\pi}{16}x^2$;

thus, the volume of a slice is $\pi\left(\dfrac{3x}{4}\right)^2 \Delta x = \dfrac{9\pi}{16}x^2 \Delta x$. The total volume of the cone is

$$\int_0^4 \dfrac{9\pi}{16}x^2 \, dx = \dfrac{9\pi}{16}\left(\dfrac{4^3}{3} - \dfrac{0^3}{3}\right) = \dfrac{36\pi}{3} = 12\pi,$$

or $\dfrac{1}{3}$ times the area of the base $(\pi 3^2)$ times height (4). Again,

note the use of the antiderivative of x^2: $\dfrac{x^3}{3}$.

V. The integral is important because the process of summing that the integral is performing is precisely what we need to do to solve various problems in various settings.

A. Suppose we are building a dam and want to know the total hydrostatic force on the face of the dam.

B. The pressure (that is, force per square foot) varies with depth. The pressure is greater near the bottom of the dam than at the top.

C. The total force is obtained by adding up how much force there is at each depth.

D. Suppose the dam is 100 feet wide and 40 feet deep. Then, we could think about dividing the face of the dam into narrow strips of Δh height for the width of the dam.

E. The amount of force on a strip at depth h is the product of the area of the strip, $100\Delta h$, and the pounds per square inch of water pressure at that depth.

F. The water pressure at a depth h is about $62.5h$ pounds per square foot.

G. Thus, the force on a strip of height Δh that lies at depth h is about $(62.5h)(100\Delta h)$ pounds, so that the total force is $\int_0^{40} (62.5h)100\,dh$.

H. We can evaluate this integral via the Fundamental Theorem of Calculus. Given that an antiderivative of h is $\dfrac{h^2}{2}$, we can calculate that

the total hydrostatic force on the face of the dam is 5,000,000 pounds.

Readings:

Any standard calculus textbook, section on applications of the integral.

Questions to Consider:

1. How does the integral help us view the area of a circle in a dynamic way?

2. Hooke's Law states that, within certain limits, the force exerted by a spring that is stretched to x units beyond its resting length is a constant times x. Suppose that for a given spring, the spring constant is 5. *Work* in physics is just force times distance. Write an integral whose value equals the work done to stretch this spring from its resting position to one that is 3 units longer. (Note: If a constant force F were applied over 3 units, the work done would simply be $3F$. With the spring, the force varies; thus, $F(x)$ is the variable force where $F(x) = 5x$, and where x is the amount the spring is stretched. The integral is perfectly designed to add up force times distance products as the distance varies from 0 to 3.)

Lecture Twelve

Buffon's Needle or π from Breadsticks

Scope: Calculus finds applications in many corners of the world, so it should come as no surprise that calculus is useful in many branches of mathematics, as well. Here, we explore an example in which calculus is used to compute a surprising result in probability. What's especially surprising is that we can compute a definite number, namely, the number π, using a random process. Random processes can lead to unrandom conclusions. In this lecture, we will explore an experiment called *Buffon's Needle*, which involves dropping needles randomly on a sheet of paper. In order to analyze this scenario, we will need to use the sine and the cosine functions, so we begin today's lecture with a review of what the sine and cosine functions are and what their derivatives and integrals are.

Outline

I. In this lecture, we will compute a definite number, namely, the number π, by exploring an experiment called *Buffon's Needle*, which involves dropping needles randomly on a sheet of paper.

II. To solve the Buffon's Needle problem, we will use the Fundamental Theorem of Calculus to compute the integral of the sine function over a certain interval. First, however, we need to get a better understanding of sine.

    A. Recall that sine is a function that is defined geometrically on the circle and that associates a number with every angle. We use radian measurement of the angle to tell us the distance along the unit circle from the point (1,0) counterclockwise up to the point in question.

    B. Sine of the angle θ is the height of a right triangle with angle θ and hypotenuse 1; the cosine is the width of that triangle.

C. As θ changes, so does the sin θ: When θ is 0, sine is 0; when θ is small, so is sin θ; when θ approaches 90 degrees (or $\frac{\pi}{2}$ in radian measurement), sin θ approaches 1.

D. More generally, the (cos θ, sin θ) are the coordinates of the point on the circle of radius 1 corresponding to the angle θ radians.

E. As we rotate our angle around the circle, the sine value varies from 0 up to 1, back to 0, down to –1, back to 0, and so forth. We can graph the sine function and see that it is an oscillating curve.

III. The cosine function is the analogous computation for the horizontal distance to every point on the circle. The cosine measure of angle 0 is 1, and it then oscillates back and forth.

IV. Now let's try to understand the derivative of sine.

A. Look at the rate at which the line opposite the hypotenuse is changing in relation to a change in the angle.

B. We ask ourselves how quickly the sine of angle θ will change as we change the angle a small amount.

C. Notice that the graph of the cosine captures the slopes of the tangent lines on the sine graph. That is a visual indication that the derivative of the sine is the cosine.

D. We use the fact that the tangent line of a circle is perpendicular to the radius and find similar right triangles in a figure of the unit circle that illustrates the sine function.

E. We see that the derivative of the sine is the cosine, and the derivative of the cosine is negative the sine.

F. From the graphs of these functions, we see geometrically why their derivatives are related as they are. Neat.

G. Now that we have derivatives of sine and cosine, by the Fundamental Theorem of Calculus, we also have their antiderivatives:

    1. An antiderivative of $\cos x$ is $\sin x$.

    2. An antiderivative of $\sin x$ is $-\cos x$.

V. We now look at something entirely different by taking a brief excursion to probability.

A. We can quantitatively describe the chance of an uncertain event.

B. For example, the chance of rolling a 3 when rolling a die is $\frac{1}{6}$.

C. In general, the probability of an event measures what percentage of the time that event will happen.

D. One way to measure probability is to do the experiment many times and just count the fraction.

E. For example, in the die case, we could roll a die many times and see what fraction of the time we get a 3.

F. I did this experiment with the help of my children. They rolled the die 1,000 times and counted 164 3s. The fraction of 3s rolled was actually $\frac{164}{1000}$, which in decimal form is 0.164. This result is close to the probability that we reasoned it must be, $\frac{1}{6}$, which in decimal form is 0.16666...

G. In general, the more times we perform an experiment, the closer the experimental fraction will be to the actual probability. This concept is called the *Law of Large Numbers*.

VI. Now we use probability and calculus to understand Buffon's Needle.

    A. The 18th-century French scientist Georges Louis Leclerc, Comte de Buffon, asked a question about a random experiment.

    B. The experiment involves dropping needles (or, in our case, breadsticks) on a lined paper.

    C. Drop a needle randomly on a lined page where the distance between lines is equal to the needle length. What is the chance that the needle will hit a line?

    D. Repeat the process of dropping the needle a number of times and count the times it hits a line. The number of times the needle crosses a line divided by the number of times we dropped the needle is a measure of the frequency with which we hit a line.

    E. If we drop the needle more and more, that measure of the frequency should get close to the actual probability.

F. What we will see is that by doing this experiment, we can estimate the value of π.

VII. We can use calculus to deduce what the exact probability should be.

    A. Let's describe where the needle could land.

    B. There are two parameters we will consider associated with each needle's landing.

        1. One is the angle at which it lands (the angular measurement). If it lands exactly parallel to the parallel lines, its angle is 0. As it rotates, we will measure its position in radial angle from 0 to π.

        2. We will also measure where the center of the needle lands relative to the lines. The center could be on the line or somewhere between the lines.

    C. For convenience, we will say that the distance between the lines and the length of the needle are both 2 units.

    D. In this way, the position and the angle tell the story.

    E. Our challenge is to see how many of those positions hit the line.

    F. If the angle is close to 0, then the center must be very close to the line to cause a hit.

    G. If the angle is about $\dfrac{\pi}{2}$, then the center can be far away and still cause a hit.

    H. Can we make that specific?

    I. For any angle θ, if the center's distance is less than sin θ, the needle will hit the line.

    J. Every angle has a particular distance where a needle at that angle first starts to encounter the line.

    K. We have, then, a rectangle describing possible positions of the needle.

    L. Within that rectangle, those positions under the $\sin\theta$ curve are positions that hit, and those above the curve are positions that don't hit.

    M. The total rectangle has area π.

N. The question is: How much area is under the curve?

O. Calculus comes to the rescue.

P. The integral of $\sin\theta$ from 0 to π is 2.

Q. Thus, the probability that the needle will hit a line is $\dfrac{2}{\pi}$.

VIII. This experiment shows a method for estimating the value of π.

A. We now know that the probability in the abstract of the needle hitting a line is $\dfrac{2}{\pi}$. If after many experiments, we find that a needle hits the line x times in y droppings, then we would expect that $\dfrac{x}{y}$ is about equal to $\dfrac{2}{\pi}$. That is, π is about equal to $\dfrac{2y}{x}$.

B. Let's see what happens with the data we collected before.
    1. When we dropped the needle 100,000 times, we hit a line 63,639 times.
    2. Using a calculator, we see that
$$\frac{2\times 100{,}000}{63{,}639} = 3.1427269\ldots,$$ quite close to π, which is 3.1415926….

C. Buffon was able to give estimates for π by, we kid you not, throwing breadsticks over his shoulder on a tiled floor and seeing how often they hit the grouting.

D. Hundreds of years after Buffon tossed his breadsticks, atomic scientists discovered that a similar needle-dropping model seems to accurately predict the chances that a neutron produced by the fission of an atomic nucleus would either be stopped or deflected by another nucleus near it—even nature appears to drop needles.

E. Buffon's Needle used calculus and gives one way of estimating π. Another way to use calculus to estimate π is by doing an infinite addition problem, as we will see later.

F. Perhaps this story could be called: *Randomly dropping a needle from the sky gives us the ability to approximate π.*

Readings:

Any standard calculus textbook, sections on applications of the definite integral.

Burger, Edward B., and Michael Starbird. *The Heart of Mathematics: An invitation to effective thinking.*

Questions to Consider:

1. In what sense do repeated trials of an experiment lead us to conclude the probability of an event happening? Why do more trials result in increasing accuracy?

2. Find a website about Buffon's Needle and try the virtual experiment.

Lecture Thirteen
Achilles, Tortoises, Limits, and Continuity

Scope: In a race between Achilles and a tortoise, the tortoise gets a head
start, say to position 1. Achilles zooms along to position 1, but the
tortoise has moved a bit forward, to position 2. Achilles proceeds
to position 2, but the tortoise, though slow, does move a bit to
position 3. Achilles must then go on to position 3, but the tortoise
has moved to position 4, and so on, forever. Zeno's paradox is that
Achilles will never pass the tortoise, because Achilles must always
catch up, while the tortoise has moved forward. Because there are
infinitely many times that Achilles must catch up, the tortoise is
confident he will win the race—that is, until Achilles passes him
by. How can the infinite number of times that Achilles remains
behind be reconciled with the experience that Achilles wins the
race? This paradox illustrates the idea of *limit*, which makes the
infinite processes in the definitions of the derivative and the
integral meaningful and precise. The notion of the limit is also
essential to understanding which kinds of functions are susceptible
to the methods of calculus and which functions are not.

Outline

I.   The *limit* plays an essential role in calculus.

    A. We could not really define derivatives or integrals without the
concept of limit.

    B. Historically speaking, however, limits were hard to formalize.
        1. The intuitive idea of limit existed since ancient times.
        2. Much of the development of calculus occurred without an
understanding of limits that today we would view as rigorous.
        3. Newton and Leibniz did not know the definition of limit.
        4. More than 150 years elapsed between the invention of
calculus and an adequate definition of limit.

II. In this lecture, we will discuss not only the limit but also continuity and
differentiability.

III. One of Zeno's paradoxes leads to an idea that is central to the mathematical underpinning of calculus—the idea of limit.

    A. The paradox involves a race between Achilles and a tortoise.

    B. The tortoise gets a head start, but Achilles zooms along and gets to the place where the tortoise started. However, the tortoise keeps moving along at the same time. Zeno's paradox is that Achilles will never pass the tortoise!

    C. The relationship between the infinite number of subjourneys and the finality of arrival captures the idea of limit.

IV. The intuitive idea of limit is that if a quantity gets closer and closer to a fixed value, then the fixed value is the limit. Thus, we can state that .999999999… (repeat 9s forever) is the same as 1.

V. The derivative and the integral entail taking limits. Let's recall what the derivative means for the function $f(x) = x^2$ at the point $x = 1$.

    A. We choose small increments of x, by tradition denoted Δx.

    B. Our notation is: $\lim\limits_{\Delta x \to 0}\left(\dfrac{f(1 + \Delta x) - f(1)}{\Delta x} \right)$.

    C. As we choose values of Δx that get closer and closer to 0, we find that the values of $\dfrac{f(1 + \Delta x) - f(1)}{\Delta x}$ are getting closer and closer to 2; hence, the derivative of $f(x) = x^2$ at $x = 1$ is equal to 2.

    D. Likewise, the integral is a limit of the approximating sums.

VI. The formal definition of limit is challenging but illustrates an interesting approach to understanding.

    A. The intuitive idea of limit is that if a quantity gets closer and closer to a fixed value, then the fixed value is the limit.

    B. For example, consider the value of the expression $\dfrac{2(x^2 - 4)}{x - 2}$ as x is chosen close to 2.

C. Plugging in such values as $x = 2.1$, $x = 2.01$, and other values getting increasingly closer to 2, we see that $\dfrac{2(x^2 - 4)}{x - 2}$ has values that get increasingly close to 8.

D. Essentially, given any tiny neighborhood of 8, no matter how small, choosing numbers for x near enough to 2 will make $\dfrac{2(x^2 - 4)}{x - 2}$ have a value in that tiny neighborhood of 8.

E. Thus, we say that the limit as x approaches 2 of the expression $\dfrac{2(x^2 - 4)}{x - 2}$ is 8.

F. The formal definition of limit makes that intuitive notion precise.

VII. The definition of limit was finally formalized in the middle of the 19th century.

   A. The formal definition of limit is the following: $\displaystyle\lim_{x \to c} f(x) = L$ means for every $\varepsilon > 0$, there exists a $\delta > 0$, such that if x differs from c by less than δ, then $f(x)$ differs from L by less than ε.

   B. This definition captures the idea that for every challenge $\varepsilon > 0$, there is a response $\delta > 0$ that satisfies a condition. Every challenge has a response.

   C. Since the limit was formally defined in the 1850s, about three students have understood it.

   D. We can apply this formula in the example we saw before: $\dfrac{2(x^2 - 4)}{x - 2}$.

VIII. Because we know that limits are essential to the methods of calculus, we can ask what functions are susceptible to the methods of calculus, that is, what functions have derivatives.

IX. One idea associated with the limit is the concept of *continuity*. To hope to have a derivative, a function must be continuous: There are no gaps and there are no sudden, discrete changes.

A. In the case of motion, position is dependent on time.

    1. From moment to moment, the position changes little by little; there are no jumps.

    2. Graphs show our position on a line at various times. Jumps on the graph showing a change in position are not physically possible. Likewise, predicted values cannot be different from the actual values of a position function.

    3. *Continuous* means that at every point along the graph, the value is predictable in the sense of being the limit of the neighboring values.

B. Graphically, a function is continuous if the graph is connected and can be drawn without lifting the pencil.

C. Consider temperature changes at a given location.

    1. Temperature may change quickly but not instantaneously.

    2. We can record these temperature data with a graph.

X. Now we come to the concept of *differentiability*. When does a function have a derivative? Not all continuous functions have a derivative.

A. A differentiable function is a function where you have a smooth curve, and if you magnify the curve, it begins to look like a straight line. Such a function has a derivative.

B. A function that takes an angled turn and does not smoothly change direction, such as the path of light being reflected in a mirror, is not a differentiable curve. It will not have a derivative.

C. Functions that have sharp points are not differentiable, for example, the stock market.

D. Graphically, a function is differentiable if it is continuous and has no "sharp points," that is, kinks or cusps.

E. It is easy to identify the graphs of functions that are not differentiable functions because they have sharp points.

F. Many functions are differentiable, including polynomials, trigonometric functions, exponential functions, logarithmic functions, and combinations of these.

G. In a precise mathematical sense, most functions are so infinitely jagged that they have no place where they are smooth enough to talk about a derivative there. Yet smooth functions have been the ones on which calculus relies and from which all the wonderful developments and understanding we have seen arose.

Readings:

Cajori, Florian. "History of Zeno's Arguments on Motion," *The American Mathematical Monthly*, Vol. 22, Nos. 1–9 (1915).

Any standard calculus textbook, explanation of the limit.

Questions to Consider:

1. How does the limit concept avoid the problem of division by 0 in the definition of the derivative?

2. Could a limiting process be used in nonmathematical settings, such as labor-management negotiations?

3. Draw a smooth function. Now modify the graph so that your function is continuous but not smooth. Finally, modify the graph so that the function is discontinuous. Which of these three do you think occurs most often in nature?

Lecture Fourteen
Calculators and Approximations

Scope: Zeno's arrow paradox shows us that an infinite addition problem, $\frac{1}{2} + \frac{1}{4} + \frac{1}{8} \dots$, results in a single number, 1. In Zeno's case, we know the answer in advance. However, for π and the square root of 5 and others, we may not know the whole decimal expansion of the number, yet we may be able to show that it is equal to a specific infinite sum, and we can approximate this sum by merely adding up, say, the first few hundred terms of the infinite sum. This is exactly what our calculators do to compute the answer when we press the sin key or square root key. Where do the infinite sums come from? Some come from calculus, and we illustrate them both graphically and numerically. We also show what happens when we ask a computer to *solve* an equation numerically. Here, an infinite process dating back to Newton's time is automated and iterated sufficiently many times to produce an answer that is as close to the true answer as needed for the application.

Outline

I. Zeno's arrow paradox considers an arrow flying through the air traveling toward your heart.

    A. The arrow goes $\frac{1}{2}$ the distance from bow to heart, then $\frac{1}{4}$ that distance, then $\frac{1}{8}$ that distance, and so on, forever.

    B. Because the arrow does, in fact, arrive at its destination, the totality of those fractions is 1. Every point between the bow and the target is passed during one of the fractional distances traveled.

C. Written as an equation, we have noted that

$$1 = \frac{1}{2} + \frac{1}{4} + \frac{1}{8} + \frac{1}{16} + \frac{1}{32} + \ldots$$

We call this an *infinite series*.

D. Notice that if we stop the summing process after hundreds or thousands or millions of terms, the sum of the distances traveled will be as close to 1 as desired. In other words, the sums of only finitely many of the fractions are as close to 1 as desired but will never equal 1.

E. The limit of the finite sums, however, is 1.

II. In the case of Zeno's arrow, we know in advance what the sum is, namely, 1; however, the real significance of infinite series is that they are used to approximate quantities that we don't otherwise know.

A. Here are some infinite series whose values involve π.

1. $\dfrac{\pi}{4} = \dfrac{1}{1} - \dfrac{1}{3} + \dfrac{1}{5} - \dfrac{1}{7} + \dfrac{1}{9} - \dfrac{1}{11} + \ldots$

2. $\dfrac{\pi^2}{6} = \dfrac{1}{1^2} + \dfrac{1}{2^2} + \dfrac{1}{3^2} + \dfrac{1}{4^2} + \dfrac{1}{5^2} + \ldots$

3. In each case, we can see how adding up the first terms of each series allows us to deduce closer and closer approximations of π.

B. Each of the above equations is obtained using calculus, but for now, we leave their genesis as a mystery.

III. Polynomials are easy to calculate because they involve only addition, subtraction, multiplication, and division. We often want to approximate a nonpolynomial by a polynomial.

A. The sine curve can be approximated by polynomials.

B. That is, we can write down an infinite polynomial that gives us the precise value of $\sin x$ for every angle x given in radians.

C. Specifically,

$$\sin x = x - \frac{x^3}{3 \times 2 \times 1} + \frac{x^5}{5 \times 4 \times 3 \times 2 \times 1} - \frac{x^7}{7 \times 6 \times 5 \times 4 \times 3 \times 2 \times 1} + \cdots$$

D. Using the more compact factorial notation, this is

$$\sin x = x - \frac{x^3}{3!} + \frac{x^5}{5!} - \frac{x^7}{7!} + \cdots$$

E. This means that we can take any number x and approximate its sine by plugging in x to the right-hand side of the equation and doing the multiplications and additions. The more terms we use, the closer we will be to the exact answer.

F. The value of the sine at any angle is equal to an infinite sum.

G. Let's consider some examples, such as the angle $30°$, which is $\frac{\pi}{6}$ radians. Notice that $\sin \frac{\pi}{6}$ (which equals $\frac{1}{2}$) is increasingly better approximated by adding more numbers in the series.

H. Let's look at various curves that are becoming increasingly like the sine curve. That is, we can compare the graph of the sine function with the graphs of the polynomials obtained by using more and more terms of the right-hand side of the equation.

I. We can see better how this process works using an example of a car moving on a straight road.

  1. Suppose the car never moves faster than 1 mile per minute per minute. If the car travels at its maximum speed, after 1 minute, the car would have traveled 1 mile.

  2. If the car starts traveling from a full stop and accelerates at 1 mile per minute per minute, then after 1 minute, the car would have gone $\frac{1}{2}$ mile.

  3. If you have a function whose derivative starts at 0, and its derivative is 0, and the derivative of that is 0, and so on with infinitely many derivatives all equal to 0, the car would not travel at all.

J. Using series is exactly how calculators compute values of trigonometric functions, such as sine.

IV. Where do these approximations come from? We can compute the first few derivatives of $\sin x$, evaluate them at $x = 0$, and write an infinite polynomial that has the same values for its derivatives evaluated at 0 as $\sin x$. This gives the following:

$$\sin x = 0 + x - 0 - \frac{x^3}{3!} + 0 + \frac{x^5}{5!} - 0 - \frac{x^7}{7!} + \ldots = x - \frac{x^3}{3!} + \frac{x^5}{5!} - \frac{x^7}{7!} + \ldots$$

V. In addition to using derivatives to compute such values as π or $\sin 1$, calculators also use derivatives in the *Newton-Raphson Method* to solve equations.

    A. The Newton-Raphson Method for approximating a solution to an equation involves making an initial guess, then using derivatives to refine the guess.

    B. Let's actually work an example of finding a root of an equation using this method. Let's try to find the square root of 5. The square root of 5 is a solution to the equation $x^2 - 5$.

        1. Let's try a first guess of 2.

        2. The method gives a second guess of 2.25, whose square is already pretty good, namely 5.0625.

        3. Using 2.25 as our next guess produces a third guess of 2.236111111…. That guess is really good, with a square of 5.000192852….

        4. Using 2.236111111… as our next guess produces a fourth guess of 2.236067978…. This is as close as my calculator gets.

    C. Now you know what really happens inside your trusty Casio, TI, IBM, or Macintosh once you press the sin or SOLVE button!

Readings:

Any standard calculus textbook, sections on infinite series and the Newton-Raphson method.

Questions to Consider:

1. Consider this infinite sum: $1 - 1 + 1 - 1 + 1 - 1 + \ldots$. Is there a single number to which it tends? Not all infinite sums converge to a number.

2. Suppose you add up an infinite number of terms and they converge to a single answer. Why must the terms that you are adding have a limit of 0? Why is that condition not a guarantee that the infinite series converges?

3. Use the Newton-Raphson Method to approximate the cube root of 2. How close can you get with your calculator?

Lecture Fifteen
The Best of All Possible Worlds—Optimization

Scope: One of the most practical applications of calculus and of derivatives in particular is *optimization*. Suppose we want to build a box that holds 8 cubic feet with material that costs $2 a square foot for the bottom, $1 per square foot for the sides, and another cost for the top. What shape will minimize the cost of the box? This type of problem brings students to tears, but it illustrates a process of enormous importance in the real world, namely, selecting, from a range of possible designs, the design that optimizes some feature—in this case, cost savings. In this lecture, we'll look at several kinds of optimization problems, including optimizing the area that can be enclosed given a certain amount of fencing and optimizing the shape of a soda can. The strategy for solving these problems involves an intriguing application of derivatives.

Outline

I. *Optimization* is one of the most practical applications of calculus and of derivatives in particular.

   A. Optimization enables us to select, from a range of possible designs, the design that optimizes some feature, perhaps cost savings, time, materials, or use of space.

   B. The strategy for solving such problems involves an intriguing application of derivatives.

   C. This kind of problem is the bane of the lives of calculus students everywhere.

II. Suppose you have 600 feet of fencing with which you want to enclose a herd of camels in a rectangular field, one edge of which is bounded by a straight river. What dimensions should you make the fence to enclose the largest possible area?

   A. The interesting strategy involved in analyzing this question is that, in a sense, we look at all possible answers at once.

   1. The question is one of trying to maximize a quantity—the area of the field.

2. Let's think about some possibilities for the shape of the field—long and narrow, tall and thin, and shapes in between. We can experiment with different choices.

B. Thinking about listing all the choices gives us the realization that any allowable choice of length and width determines an area.
  1. The area depends on length and width.
  2. The width can be any value from 0 (laying the fence right along the riverbank) to 300 (having the fence just go up and back right next to itself).
  3. Of course, the answer will lie somewhere in between.

III. Calculus is, of course, the hero or heroine.

A. The clever strategy is to ask a question about *change* in area (as a function of *change* in width), rather than the more natural question about values of the area.

B. If we make a guess for an optimal width, what would be the effect on the area if we changed our guess a little?
  1. A change in width results in a change in the area, because the area is determined once we know the width.
  2. This situation is exactly what calculus is for.
  3. Calculus (in particular, the derivative) deals with cases where the change in one quantity produces a change in another.

C. For example, suppose we make the reasonable guess that the optimal shape for the field would be a square. The area would be 40,000 square feet.
  1. If we change the dimensions to 201(length) × 198(width), we have an area of 39,798 sq ft, so we know the square has more square feet.
  2. However, if we change again to 199(length) × 202(width), the square footage is 40,198. Thus, we know the square is not the optimal fencing shape.
  3. All possible configurations of the area enclosed within the fence can be expressed in the following formula, where $w =$ width:
$$A(w) = (600 - 2w) \times w = 600w - 2w^2$$

IV. Let's organize the possible widths and areas in a convenient form.

A. For every choice of width, we can record the area by graphing the function of area as it depends on width.

B. Looking at the graph of possible areas, it is easy to pick out by eye the maximum area; it's the one on top.

C. Notice that at that peak point, the blown-up picture of the graph would look like a horizontal line.

D. When the graph looks like a horizontal line, the derivative is 0.

E. Thus, we know that the maximum area will occur at a point where the derivative is 0.

F. How can we find a point where the derivative is 0? The answer is to find an expression for the derivative and set it equal to 0.

    1. In this case, the derivative of $600w - 2w^2$ is $600 - 4w$.

    2. We set the derivative equal to 0 and solve for w, as follows:

$$0 = 600 - 4w$$
$$4w = 600$$
$$w = 150$$

V. Here is an overview of our method:

A. The strategy for finding the maximum area was not to compute the area for different values of possible widths.

B. Instead, we considered the whole collection of possible areas created by all possible choices of widths.

C. Among those, we looked for a value of the width at which the rate of change of the area with respect to width was 0.

D. In other words, we looked for features of the dependency of the area on the width. In particular, we looked at the rate of change of the area when the width was changed and found a place where the rate of change was 0.

VI. This strategy of finding *maxima* and *minima* is extremely useful.

A. The strategy is to realize that *maxima* and *minima* will occur at places where the derivative is 0.

B. Generally, in a graph there aren't very many places where that happens, so we don't have too many values to look at.

C. This max-min strategy is valuable in many settings.

VII. Here is an optimization problem from human physiology: When we cough, the trachea (windpipe) contracts to increase the velocity of the air going out. How much does it contract to achieve the maximum velocity for the escaping air?

A. Biologists have observed that a good model for the velocity of the air escaping from the trachea as a function of its radius is given by the equation $v(r) = c(r_0 r^2 - r^3)$, where c is a constant and r_0 is the radius of the trachea at rest.

B. The strategy is then to find where $v'(r)$ is zero:

$v'(r) = c(2r_0 r - 3r^2) = 0$ exactly when $r = \dfrac{2}{3} r_0$, that is, when

the trachea is about $\dfrac{2}{3}$ contracted.

C. Amazingly x-ray photographs confirm this observation!

VIII. Our final example comes from product design.

A. Suppose we are designing a soda can that is to hold 12 fluid ounces. What dimensions minimize the amount of aluminum used?

B. We will assume that our soda can is cylindrical.

C. If it has base radius r and height h, its volume is $V = \pi r^2 h$ and its surface area is $A = 2\pi rh + 2\pi r^2$.

D. One fluid ounce is approximately 1.8 cubic inches, so our volume V is 21.6 cubic inches.

E. Solving for h, $h = \dfrac{21.6}{\pi r^2}$, and substituting into the equation for

A, we find $A = \dfrac{43.2}{r} + 2\pi r^2$.

F. Finding the derivative, setting it to zero, and solving for r, we find $r = 1.51$ inches, which in turn, yields $h = 3.02$ inches.

G. Does this agree with the actual dimensions of soda cans?

H. In reality, many other factors must be taken into consideration when designing soda cans, changing the function to be optimized and, thus, resulting in different measurements.

Readings:

Any standard calculus textbook, section on max-min problems.

Questions to Consider:

1. Find two numbers such that their sum is 20 and their product is maximum.

2. Issues of balance and proportion are often problems of maximizing or minimizing something. What is the balance of daily activities, such as work, social activity, and exercise, that maximizes happiness? Do you think that the philosophy of the mathematical strategy for finding maxima and minima is useful when considering such completely nonmathematical issues as human happiness?

Lecture Sixteen
Economics and Architecture

Scope: In this lecture, we illustrate optimization in the context of economics and architecture. For example, revenue and cost are two fundamental quantities any firm considers, and the difference between the two is the firm's profit. The firm must select the number of items to produce so as to maximize profit: We show that the optimal number of items to produce is exactly where marginal revenue equals marginal cost. We then turn our attention to architecture, where we look at arch structures. We conclude with a glimpse into the calculus of variations, which is a method of finding the optimal curve, that is, a function, rather than just an optimal number for a certain problem.

Outline

I. Many aspects of business and economic conditions are described by functions that relate one feature of the situation to another. Heads of business wish to optimize and maximize the profits for their companies.

A. Remember: Maximization is a process that calls for calculus!

B. The cost function $C(x)$ tells us how much it costs to produce x items.

C. The revenue function $R(x)$ tells us the total revenue expected if we sell x items.

D. Profit $P(x)$ is simply the revenue minus the cost:

$P(x) = R(x) - C(x)$. Our job is to maximize that difference.

E. If we change the number of items produced, the change in the cost can be measured as a derivative of the cost curve. The change in cost is called the marginal cost, MC, and it measures the additional cost of producing one more item when x are already produced. MC is the derivative of the cost function.

F. Similarly, the marginal revenue, MR, is the rate at which the revenue grows, and it measures the additional revenue we get by selling one more item when x are already sold. MR is the derivative of the revenue function.

II. The maximum profit will occur when the marginal cost and the marginal revenue are equal. Why?

    A. If, at a particular production level, the marginal revenue is greater than the marginal cost, then producing one more item will yield greater profit—the increase in revenue will exceed the increase in cost.

    B. On the other hand, if the marginal cost is greater than the marginal revenue, then decreasing production will lead to more profit, because the cost will be reduced more than the revenue is reduced.

    C. Mathematically, we know that the maximum of the function $P(x)$ occurs where $P'(x) = 0$. However,

$$P'(x) = MR(x) - MC(x) = 0 \text{ exactly when } MR = MC.$$

       Thus, mathematical reasoning agrees with our intuitive understanding.

III. Here is an example of a business problem with the goal of choosing production and price levels that will maximize profit.

    A. Suppose our company wishes to manufacture and sell a product.

    B. The fixed cost for designing and modifying manufacturing equipment is $100,000.

    C. After those fixed expenses, the cost for producing and marketing the item is $30 per unit.

    D. Experience has shown that if the items are sold at price p, then approximately $20,000 - 50p$ will be sold. Notice that this means that if the price is $400, no one will buy any, and if the price is extremely low, about 20,000 people will buy them.

    E. As we have learned, MC is 30. MR, a somewhat more complicated figure, is calculated to be $400 - \dfrac{x}{25}$.

    F. What price should be set, and how many items should be manufactured? The answer is 9,250 at a price of $215 each.

IV. Even an architectural issue, such as where to stand to get the best view of a painting in a museum, is a problem of maxima and minima.

    A. First, we need to draw a picture to see what we are trying to optimize.

    B. In this case, we are looking to optimize the angle at which we can best view the painting; therefore, our goal is to find the distance from the wall at which the angle is biggest.

    C. Once again, we use the derivative—in this case, the derivative of the arc tangent—to arrive at the answer.

    D. A similar calculation can be effective in determining where to sit at a movie theater to optimize the angle to the screen.

V. Challenge problems were a feature of European mathematics in the 17th century. We'll look briefly at two such questions.

    A. One such problem was to find an equation to describe the shape of a hanging chain.

        1. Galileo had mistakenly thought that such a chain hung in the shape of a parabola, but Jungius, another mathematician, had disproved that proposition in 1669.

        2. In 1690, Jakob Bernoulli posed the challenge to find the correct equation for the shape, and his challenge was solved by Huygens, Johann Bernoulli, and Leibniz in 1691; of course, the solution used calculus.

        3. The shape is called a *catenary*, and it has several interesting properties.

            a. The horizontal forces on each link are in equilibrium. An inverted catenary is a particularly good shape for an arch because the forces are tangential along the arch. A beautiful example of an inverted catenary arch is the St. Louis Arch.

            b. A strange property of the catenary is that if you made a road of inverted catenaries, you could ride a bicycle with square wheels on that road and be perfectly level.

        4. Galileo was almost right about the parabola shape.

            a. A catenary and a parabola are similar in shape, and a catenary actually turns into a parabola if you construct a bridge using hanging cables, then suspend weights evenly along it.

> **b.** For example, at the Golden Gate Bridge in San Francisco, the tension in the cable must support a certain load, so the arch that was a catenary became a parabola after the road was hung from it.

B. The other challenge problem is called the *Brachistochrone problem*. In 1696, Johann Bernoulli posed the problem; namely, down what shaped curve between two points would a ball reach the lower point fastest?

   1. Newton was tired from a hard day at the mint when he received the problem. Because he was intrigued and annoyed by the problem, he stayed up until 4:00 a.m. until he had solved it.

   2. Five people solved the Brachistochrone problem correctly, and all are famous in calculus: Johann Bernoulli, Jakob Bernoulli, the Marquis de L'Hôpital, Leibniz, and Newton.

   3. The solution is a cycloid, which is a curve created by a rolling wheel.

   4. A straight line is not the answer.

      a. We can perform the experiment to demonstrate this fact.

      b. Intuitively, it is reasonable to think that if the curve starts steeply down, the ball will gain velocity faster.

   5. This curve is also called an *isochrone* because, no matter where on the curve you release the ball, it arrives at the end at the same time.

VI. Virgil's *Aeneid* refers to an optimization problem now known as *Dido's problem*.

A. Queen Dido was granted the amount of land that could be enclosed by an ox's hide.

B. She cut the hide into a long, thin strip and made a large circle.

C. How do we know that the circle encloses the biggest area given the length of the string?

D. The solution to the optimization question is to find the pattern of a curve and not just a number.

E. The solutions to this problem and the Brachistochrone problem involve a method of calculus known as *calculus of variations*.

Readings:

Any calculus textbooks on applications to economics and calculus of variations.

Questions to Consider:

1. Recall your last trip to the supermarket. What function are you optimizing as you shop for groceries? What is your constraint for the optimization? Do you think it's possible to write down equations for both functions?

2. What other shapes, coming from nature or architecture, do you think solve some kind of a physical optimization problem? (Think of arches, for example.)

Lecture Seventeen
Galileo, Newton, and Baseball

Scope: One of the most direct applications of calculus concerns the description of moving objects. It is vitally important to be able to predict where a projectile will land and what path it will take. Certainly in using any military device, such as a cannon, we need to know the path of the cannonball so we can figure out where to aim it. Perhaps more important, an outfielder needs to know where to stand to catch a fly ball. Galileo performed a famous experiment at the Tower of Pisa to demonstrate a feature of the velocity at which falling bodies fall; Kepler studied planetary motion; and Newton devised a general theory of gravitation. All these examples illustrate how methods of calculus can describe the path and velocity of projectiles from cannonballs to baseballs to planets.

Outline

I. One of the most direct applications of calculus concerns the prediction of where a projectile, whether a cannonball or baseball, will land and what path it will take. The work of Galileo, Kepler, and Newton all illustrate how methods of calculus can describe the path and velocity of projectiles.

II. Aristotle wrote that heavier objects fall faster than lighter ones.

  A. Galileo refuted Aristotle's assertions by direct experiment. He may or may not have dropped balls from the Tower of Pisa to show that heavier bodies do not fall faster than lighter ones.

  B. In a vacuum, a feather falls exactly as fast as an iron ball.

  C. Galileo devised a formula for how far a body will fall in a given amount of time.

  D. Galileo also formulated the idea that a body in motion will tend to remain in motion at the same velocity and in the same direction until some force acts on it.

III. In 1665, the plague closed Cambridge University and Newton spent a couple of years on his family farm thinking about mathematics and the universe. (Perhaps years with less instruction would improve our creativity, as well.)

A. Newton devised the law of universal gravitation, namely, that the force of gravity between any two objects is proportional to the product of their masses and inversely proportional to the square of their distance apart.

B. A falling apple actually may have suggested to Newton the idea that the force pulling the apple was the same as the force holding the Moon or the planets in orbit.

C. Newton also formulated other laws of physics, the first one following Galileo.

    1. A body in motion will stay in motion unless a force is applied to it.

    2. The second law is written $F = ma$. This law connects force (such as gravity) to acceleration. A uniform force applied to a body creates a uniform acceleration.

    3. The third law is stated: For every action, there is an equal and opposite reaction.

D. From the inverse square law of gravitation and his other laws of motion, Newton was able to deduce Kepler's laws of planetary motion, including the fact that the planets revolve around the Sun in elliptical orbits.

IV. Using Newton's laws, we can analyze the motion of a falling body.

A. The force of gravity at the surface of the Earth will cause a body to accelerate at about –32 feet per second per second, where the minus sign indicates that the acceleration is in the downward direction.

B. From this insight, we can conclude that a falling body will accelerate at a constant rate. That is, if we drop a ball, after 1 second, it will be traveling –32 ft/sec; after 2 seconds, –64 ft/sec; after 3 seconds, –96 ft/sec; and so on.

C. Notice that it is the velocity that is increasing with each second. The distance traveled is increasing far more each second.

D. It is an easy matter, then, to write down the velocity of the object at each second. Namely, $-32t$ ft/sec, where t is the time in seconds since the ball was dropped.

E. Now we can use our insights about the relation between distance traveled and velocity to compute the distance the falling ball will have fallen after any given amount of time.

   1. Notice that $-16t^2$ is a position function that would give $-32t$ as the velocity at each time, because the derivative of $-16t^2$ is $-32t$.

   2. The distance that the ball falls after t seconds is $-16t^2$.

   3. After 3 seconds, the ball will have fallen $-16(3^2) = -144$ feet.

V. Throwing balls lets us analyze the paths that projectiles take.

   A. Let's first consider throwing a ball straight up, then catching it. Let's say the initial velocity is 48 ft/sec.

   B. If we throw the ball up at v_0 ft/sec, then the velocity will decrease at 32 ft/sec each second, where a negative velocity is the velocity at which the ball will fall after it reaches its peak height.

   1. Thus, the velocity at time t will be $v_0 - 32t$ ft/sec.

   2. For example, if we throw the ball up at 48 ft/sec, it will rise for 1.5 seconds before it reaches its highest point. At 1.5 seconds, its velocity will be 0 right before it descends.

   C. The height of the ball at time t will be $v_0 t - 16t^2$; that is a position function whose derivative would yield the velocity we know we have at each time, namely, $v_0 - 32t$.

VI. Let's analyze the path of a fly ball with the help of a graph.

   A. Putting these ideas together, a ball thrown or hit at a certain velocity upward (in this case, 48 ft/sec) and a certain velocity forward (100 ft/sec) will rise and fall along a curved path.

   B. The height at each second t is given by $v_0 t - 16t^2$, where v_0 is the initial vertical velocity.

   C. We know the ball will land when the height of the ball is 0 again. Using the calculation $48t - 16t^2 = 0$, we find that the ball will land after 3 seconds.

D. The horizontal velocity will be a steady velocity equal to the initial horizontal velocity. Therefore, after 3 seconds, the ball will land 300 feet away from home plate (100 ft/sec × 3 sec).

E. Consider a fly ball. How does the outfielder know where to stand to be in the place where the ball will land?

    1. The answer is neat. At each moment, the outfielder can measure the slope of the line from the outfielder's eye to the ball.

    2. If the rate at which the slope is changing is a constant, that is, the derivative of the slope of the line to the moving ball is a constant, then the ball will land right in the outfielder's eye.

    3. Perhaps Willie Mays was doing calculus when he made an incredible catch in the 1954 World Series, winning the series for the New York Giants.

F. Another way to catch the ball would be available to a baseball player who was playing on a more theoretical field.

    1. Suppose the batter hit the ball, but the Earth itself was not there. Instead, suppose that all the mass of the Earth were concentrated in a single point at the center of the Earth.

    2. The baseball would then take on an elliptical orbit around that point.

    3. It would zoom down, whip around the concentrated center of the Earth, and return.

    4. The outfielder could leisurely stroll up to where the batter hit the ball and simply wait.

    5. In about half an hour, the ball would return, traveling at precisely the velocity at which it was hit but coming from the opposite direction.

G. Conclusion: Every outfielder knows calculus.

Readings:

Any standard calculus textbook, section on falling bodies.

Questions to Consider:

1. If you are skeptical that every outfielder knows calculus, then how does the outfielder know where to run?

2. Is it surprising to you that such an easily contradicted assertion, such as Aristotle's assertion about heavy bodies falling faster, could nevertheless be believed for centuries?

©2006 The Teaching Company.

Lecture Eighteen
Getting off the Line—Motion in Space

Scope: Cars do not really drive in straight lines. They move about on roads that turn. A mosquito flying through the air has a position at each moment that is varying in all three spatial dimensions. Planets move around the Sun. After developing the ideas of calculus for cars moving in a straight line, we have gained enough experience and expertise to apply the same methods of reasoning to things moving around anywhere in space. We can ask all the same questions that we considered when talking about the simple case of cars on straight roads. We can talk about their instantaneous velocity and we can ask how far they travel. One of the strengths of calculus is its versatility. Ideas developed in simple settings can be modified and expanded to apply in more complicated settings.

Outline

I. How can we describe motion in space?

    A. At each moment in time, a flying mosquito is at some specific position in space.

    B. That position can be described by three spatial coordinates.

    C. The position of the moving mosquito is an example in which each time yields a more complicated quantity than just a single number.

    D. Each time yields all three spatial coordinates.

II. Let's consider an example of a bug (VW, that is) moving around a plane.

    A. Notice that the positions are time-stamped, so we know where the bug was at each moment.

    B. Specifically, we know its *x*- and *y*-coordinates at each time.

    C. Here are some questions we can consider:

        1. In what direction is the bug going at each moment?

        2. How fast is the bug moving at each moment?

        3. The combination of these two pieces of information—the direction the bug is moving and the velocity with which it's moving—is the velocity vector of the bug.

4. How far did the bug travel? This last question seeks the length of a curved path.

D. These are all calculus questions.

III. Let's revisit the scenario of the trajectory of a baseball.

A. Recall that the position of the moving ball can be given by stating at each time how far it has moved horizontally and how high it is. Therefore, this is a *vector-valued function.*

B. Specifically, suppose the ball leaves the bat with a horizontal velocity of 100 feet per second and a vertical velocity of 48 ft/sec.

1. As we learned in Lecture Seventeen, at any time t seconds after being hit, the ball will be located $48t - 16t^2$ feet up in the air and $100t$ feet horizontally from the plate.

2. At any time t seconds after being hit, the ball will have vertical velocity $48 - 32t$, because gravity is changing the vertical velocity by 32 ft/sec downward during each second of travel. Its horizontal velocity will continue to be 100 ft/sec.

C. From this information, we can compute how fast the ball is actually traveling at every moment and in what direction.

D. To find that out, we find derivatives, one of which will give us the rate at which the ball is moving horizontally and one of which will give us the rate at which the ball is moving vertically.

E. We combine those two rates to find the actual velocity and direction of the ball.

F. To combine the motion in the two directions, we make use of a right triangle and the Pythagorean Theorem.

1. We have one component of velocity in the horizontal direction (v_x) and another in the vertical direction (v_y).

2. To find the diagonal length of the triangle, which represents the speed at which the ball is moving at any time and in any direction, we take the square root of $v_{[x]}(t)^2 + v_{[y]}(t)^2$.

3. We can compute this value for a variety of times and vertical velocities.

IV. We found the velocity and direction of travel of a car; however, we have not yet figured out how far it travels over time.

A. In this case, the car's x coordinate is the horizontal component

$$p_{[x]}(t) = \frac{t^3}{3} - t.$$ Its y coordinate is $p_{[y]}(t) = t^2$. We consider t as measured in minutes and p as measured in miles.

B. The distance traveled is the same as the length of a curved path.

C. Let's obtain an approximation of the distance the car traveled from time 0 to time 3.

    1. At each time, we can find the velocity at which we are traveling, as described before, by taking derivatives in each coordinate and using the Pythagorean Theorem.

    2. We can approximate the distance traveled in a short amount of time by multiplying the velocity times a small increment of time.

    3. We can choose small increments of time between 0 and 3, such as increments of a hundredth of a minute.

    4. By adding up the small increments of distance traveled in each hundredth of a minute, we obtain an approximation of the total distance the car traveled from time 0 to time 3.

    5. This whole process is naturally represented as an integral, because the distance traveled is approximated by taking sums that are in the form of the integral.

D. Finding the lengths of curves is generally accomplished by using an integral.

V. Let's close with a word about the Pythagorean Theorem.

A. We have used it several times, but we have not proven it. We can do so in a number of ways.

B. The 12th-century Indian mathematician Bhaskara provided an exceptionally elegant demonstration of the truth of the Pythagorean Theorem that we can understand best with a simple diagram.

Readings:

Any standard calculus textbook, sections on vector calculus.

Questions to Consider:

1. Explain why the positions of yourself at every moment during your life form an example of a vector-valued function.

2. In English, explain the relationship between the velocity and position of the motion of the second hand versus the motion of a minute hand on a standard clock.

Lecture Nineteen
Mountain Slopes and Tangent Planes

Scope: The volume of a box depends on its length, width, and height. In other words, the volume of the box is a quantity that depends on several features, each of which can vary independently. This situation of a single value being dependent on several others is another arena in which to explore the strategies of thought that make up the world of calculus. Here, the representation of the dependency produces intriguing pictures in several dimensions. The derivative measures how much the change in one varying quantity will affect another dependent quantity. We also analyze how changes in each of several factors individually influence the whole result. The idea of a partial derivative is essential to the study of relationships involving several varying quantities.

Outline

I. In this lecture, we will study situations in which one value is dependent on two or more independently varying values.

   A. This concept is called a *function of several variables*.

   B. We will take the concepts of calculus, particularly the derivative, and see how to adapt them to functions of several variables.

II. Measuring the altitude at different places is a good example of a quantity (the altitude) that varies according to position, which is given by two coordinates (latitude and longitude).

   A. Imagine that we are standing on a mountain. The mountain has varying steepness depending on where we are and which direction we turn.

   B. The steepness refers to change in altitude with respect to a change in position, but here, the position can change in many ways, unlike the case of a car moving on a straight road.

   C. This leads to an idea of measuring the change in any direction we consider—a directional derivative.

   D. Think about expanding the location on the side of the mountain. In a small enough region, it is flat, a plane.

III. Let's explore the area of a rectangle.

 A. A rectangle is a simple shape. Its area is length times width
  ($A = l \times w$).

 B. Its area depends on two choices; thus, we can ask:
  1. How fast is the area changing with respect to a change in the
   length?
  2. How fast is the area changing with respect to a change in the
   width?

 C. If we have a rectangle 2 units wide × 5 units long, we could add a
  small amount to its length and see that the area would increase
  slightly, as well.

 D. In this case, we could ask, "What is the rate at which the area is
  increasing for a unit increase in length?" or we could ask, "What is
  the rate at which the area is increasing for a unit increase in
  width?"

 E. These two rates of change in the total when the variables are
  altered individually are called *partial derivatives*.

 F. When we change the length by Δl, how much additional area do
  we get? We see that we get Δl times the width. If we divide that
  incremented area by the change in the length, we see that the rate
  of change in the area per unit change in length is w.

 G. If we change the length of our rectangle by 1 unit, we see that we
  will increase the area by only 2 units per additional unit of length.
  Likewise, if we change the width of our rectangle by 1 unit, we see
  that we will increase the area by 5 units per additional unit of
  width.

IV. Suppose we alter both the length and the width at once.

 A. Suppose we simultaneously increase the length and width the same
  amount, 1 unit each?

 B. We can calculate the rate at which the area of the rectangle will
  increase for such a change. This is an example of a *directional
  derivative*.

V. Let us now look at the function $f(x, y) = -(x^2 + y^2)$. The analog of
 the tangent line is the tangent plane.

A. When we had a graph, it was natural to magnify it and see that it became more like a straight line.

B. When we have two variables, when we magnify the graph, it becomes more like a plane.

C. This gives the idea of a tangent plane.

D. We can interpret the partial derivatives with respect to x and with respect to y of this function.

    1. For the function $f(x, y)$, at any given point, if we stand at the point (x, y) and we move in the positive x direction, we are fixing the y coordinate, so the y direction is a constant. Thus, we are seeing the rate at which we are rising and falling. Computing that rate would be the partial derivative with respect to x.

    2. Likewise, if we stand at the point (x, y) and we move in the positive y direction, we are fixing the x coordinate, so the x direction is a constant. In this case, we are computing the partial derivative with respect to y.

    3. These partial derivatives with respect to x and with respect to y tell us geometric features about the graph of the terrain.

E. A tangent plane is that plane that contains the tangent line in the x direction and the tangent line in the y direction—lines whose slopes are determined by the partial derivatives.

F. Finding where tangent planes are horizontal locates places where the values might be maximum or minimum.

    1. Such places would indicate a peak or a downward-facing peak.

    2. In other words, if we find a place where both the partial derivatives with respect to x and with respect to y are 0, we would say that is a candidate for a maximum or minimum point.

VI. Real-world situations often involve several variables.

A. Our weight is dependent on how much we eat, what we eat, genetic factors, and how much we exercise.

B. Our bank balances are the result of two variables, how much we earn and how much we spend.

C. Many complicated situations are dependent on many variables.

D. The methods of calculus give a strategy for analyzing such situations.

Readings:

Any standard calculus textbook, chapters on functions of several variables.

Questions to Consider:

1. Choose an everyday phenomenon and describe how it can be viewed as a function of several variables. For example, the price of a stock may depend on performance of the company, global money supply, fads, and so on.

2. How could we visualize (as a graph does) a function of three variables?

Lecture Twenty
Several Variables—Volumes Galore

Scope: We have seen that integration is a way to measure area and volume. In this lecture, we extend our techniques to measure volumes and surface areas of solids obtained by a process of revolution, and we construct a theoretical solid that has finite volume but infinite surface area—that is, we have a full can of paint that does not hold enough paint to paint its own walls! Solids of revolution are nice and regular, but how can we measure volumes of stranger objects? To do this, we introduce integration in several variables, thus extending the second main idea of calculus from a line to space. Both the derivative and the integral have rich applications in settings of higher dimensions.

Outline

I. We have extended the ideas of calculus to functions of more than one variable, including analogs of the derivative.

II. Now, we will discuss computing the volumes of *solids of revolution*.

   A. Suppose that we rotate around the *x*-axis the area under a curve $f(x)$ between points a and b. The specific function we will look at is $f(x) = x^2$.

   B. The radius of each disk at a point x is then $f(x)$ or x^2, so the volume of a thin slab is just the area of a disk of radius x^2 slightly thickened. The volume of the thin hockey puck is $\pi(x^2)^2 \Delta x$.

   C. Consequently, the volume of our solid is approximated by adding up those volumes. In the limit, that sum is the integral:

   $$V = \int_a^b \pi(f(x))^2 \, dx = \int_a^b \pi(x^2)^2 \, dx \,.$$

   D. Now, suppose we have a weirdly shaped but symmetrical vase, with its shape given by the function $f(x) = x^2$ between $a = 0$ and $b = 2$.

E. At each point x, its radius is just x^2, so its volume is
$V = \int_0^2 \pi(x^2)^2 \, dx$, which with a little bit of work, evaluates to $\pi \dfrac{32}{5}$.

F. The same volume can be computed by viewing the volume as the sum of cylinders.

G. In this case, for each y between 0 and 4, we have a boundary of a "tuna can" of radius y and height $2 - \sqrt{y}$. Thickening up that cylinder slightly, by thickness Δy, at location y, gives a volume of $2\pi y(2 - \sqrt{y})\Delta y$.

H. Adding up those pieces of volume and passing to the limit gives us an integral whose value is the volume of that solid of revolution, namely, $\int_0^4 2\pi y(2 - \sqrt{y}) \, dy$, which as expected, has the same value as the previous integral, $\pi \dfrac{32}{5}$.

III. Solids of revolution also provide us with contradictory objects, including one that has finite volume but infinite surface area. This apparently nonexistent object involves the use of infinity.

    A. The object is an infinite horn obtained by revolving a curve around the x-axis.

    B. We can estimate the area and the volume of the infinite horn.

    C. Using the Fundamental Theorem of Calculus, we conclude that the total volume is finite; in fact, we discover that the volume is π cubic units.

    D. To see that there is infinite area, we divide the surface of the horn into pieces.

        1. Each piece is larger than a corresponding cylinder.

        2. Each of the infinitely many cylinders has area π; hence, the horn has infinite area.

    E. Therefore, this horn, if put upright, would be a can that would hold only π gallons of paint, yet we could not paint its walls!

F. Integrals can be used to compute the volume and area of this infinite horn.

G. This solid with infinite surface area but finite volume shows that infinity can be a tricky place to sell paint.

IV. We now look at how to extend the concept of integration to functions of two variables.

A. Recall that the integral for a regular function gave the area under the curve.

B. For a function of two variables, the integral gives the volume under the surface.

    1. A surface is the graph of a function with two variables.

    2. We can consider them in analogy to the familiar case of only one variable.

    3. Our strategy is to divide the volume into slices that run parallel to one of the axes, compute the volume of each slice using an integral, and add those together, again using an integral. Thus, we use a *double integral*.

C. In other words, computing a double integral requires us to perform an iterated process of integration.

D. The notation is really neat—a double integral symbol, for example: $\iint f(x,y)dxdy$.

E. Here's an example: Suppose we want to compute the volume contained beneath the graph of the function of two variables over a particular rectangle in the plane where the x values are between 0 and 2 and the y values are between 0 and 3; that is, $\iint_R x^2 y\,dxdy$, where $R = [0,2] \times [0,3]$.

    1. Our double integral becomes a matter of taking a single integral with respect to y, where at each value of y, the value we want to add is itself computed by taking an integral.

    2. Here is the equation: $\iint_R x^2 y\,dxdy = \int_0^3 \left(\int_0^2 x^2 y\,dx \right) dy$.

3. Alternatively, we can take a single integral with respect to y:

$$\iint\limits_R x^2 y\, dx\, dy = \int_0^2 \left(\int_0^3 x^2 y\, dy \right) dx$$

4. Through our calculations, we arrive at the same answer for both equations: 12.
5. We can think of our volume like a loaf of bread and compute the double integral by adding up thickened slices.

F. We can conclude that calculus is the best thing since sliced bread!

Readings:

Any standard calculus textbook, chapters on solids of revolution and functions of several variables.

Questions to Consider:

1. The integral $\int_0^2 \pi x^2\, dx$ represents the volume of what geometric object? Can you compute it?

2. Do you think it's possible to construct a horn with finite surface area but infinite volume?

3. The temperature of a rectangular plate at each point (x,y) is given by the function $T(x, y)$. How would you compute the average temperature of the plate?

Lecture Twenty-One
The Fundamental Theorem Extended

Scope: You will recall that after we introduced the derivative and integral, our next step was to describe their relationship via the Fundamental Theorem of Calculus. In this lecture, we'll talk about extensions of the Fundamental Theorem of Calculus that apply to our extended notions of derivatives and integrals in curved paths and several dimensions. In particular, we will study the *Fundamental Theorem for Line Integrals*, and we will look into the background of George Green, the brilliant but largely self-taught man who developed the theorem that bears his name.

Outline

I. Recall that the Fundamental Theorem of Calculus connects the derivative with the integral. Basically, it observes that the accumulation of small changes (the integral) is equal to the net effect.

  A. We first saw the Fundamental Theorem of Calculus illustrated in the motion of a car.

   1. Suppose a car is moving on a straight road and its position at each time t is given by $p(t)$.

   2. We noticed that there are two ways of finding the net distance the car traveled between time a and time b.

   3. On the one hand, the distance is $p(b) - p(a)$. On the other hand, that distance equals the integral of the velocity. And the velocity is the derivative of the position function.

   4. Thus, the Fundamental Theorem of Calculus states that
   $$\int_a^b v(t)dt = \int_a^b p'(t)dt = p(b) - p(a).$$

  B. In general then, the Fundamental Theorem of Calculus states that for any differentiable function
  $$F(x), \ \int_a^b F'(x)dx = F(b) - F(a).$$

  C. The Fundamental Theorem of Calculus can be rephrased as: "Accumulated change equals net effect."

II. With regard to a mountain slope, we considered functions of two variables. That is, for each point in the plane, we associate a number. Here, we examine what variations on the Fundamental Theorem might apply to this setting.

   A. To ground our discussion in a real situation, suppose we have a map that tells us the height of the terrain. At each point on the map, we could associate the altitude or elevation at that point, such that the map acts as a function of two variables, the x and y coordinates of that point on the map.

   B. Surveyors used to start at a point at sea level, then go a short distance and measure the rise or fall at that point, then go another short distance and repeat the measurement, and so forth. This method is suggestive of an integral because it accumulates the change in altitude.

   C. Consider the following scenario. We start at one point and draw some circuitous path on the map.

   D. There are two ways to compute the net change in altitude from start to finish.

   1. If we could measure our altitude at the beginning and the end, then of course, we could simply subtract.

   2. Another method would be to see how steep it is at every step, then compute how much we rise or fall with each step on the map and add up those changes to get the total change.

   3. This method of adding up the increases and decreases in altitude is reminiscent of the method that surveyors used to measure the altitude of mountains and the whole terrain.

   E. We can formulate this insight to give us a variation on the Fundamental Theorem of Calculus.

   1. Suppose we have a function of two variables $f(x, y)$. Think about the function that tells the altitude at each point on a map.

   2. Now we draw a path on the plane or the map.

   3. The value at the end minus the value at the beginning (the net change in altitude) is equal to the integral taken along the path of the incline at each point.

   4. The incline at each point just means the steepness at each point in the direction that we are walking. The partial

derivative with respect to x of $f(x, y)$ at a particular point on the map tells us how steep the terrain is if we took a step in the positive x direction. Likewise, the partial derivative with respect to y of $f(x, y)$ at a particular point on the map tells us how steep the terrain is if we took a step in the positive y direction.

5. If we take a step diagonally, c units in the x direction and d units in the y direction, we can estimate how high we rise by multiplying the partial derivative with respect to x times c units and adding it to the partial derivative with respect to y times d units.

6. In other words, if we take that incline or slope and multiply by the length of each step on the map, we are really taking an integral along the path—the integral of the function that tells us the rate of change of the altitude at each point, that is, the slope or steepness at each point.

7. That integral is called a *line integral* because we are doing our familiar process of adding function value times small length, but we're doing it along a path or a potentially curvy line rather than just along the x-axis.

F. We can phrase a variation of the Fundamental Theorem of Calculus in this setting by saying that the line integral of the function that tells the steepness at each point along a path from one time to another equals the difference of the altitude at the end minus the altitude at the beginning of the path.

G. Notice that taking this line integral along *any* path between two points will result in the same value.

H. The technical notation for this *Fundamental Theorem for Line Integrals* is: $\int_C \nabla f \cdot dp = f(p(b)) - f(p(a))$.

III. Calculus is used to model and describe many physical phenomena.

A. One example is the behavior of fluids and gases.

1. For instance, how would we describe the situation of the wind blowing?

2. We can measure its velocity and direction at each point. This gives a velocity vector field at each moment in time.

B. Now let's think about a region of space bounded by a surface. For example, we can think about space bounded by a sphere.

C. There is a mathematical statement that is a variation of the Fundamental Theorem of Calculus that helps us understand this situation. This version of the Fundamental Theorem of Calculus is called the *Divergence Theorem*.

D. As always, the Fundamental Theorem compares the accumulation of change to a net effect. In this case, we need to describe what change we are talking about and what net effect we are talking about.

    1. The change refers to a local analysis at each point in the region of space that describes the rate at which the gas is expanding or contracting at that point.

    2. The net effect refers to the volume of gas that is crossing the containing surface per unit time.

IV. Two other variations of the Fundamental Theorem, *Green's Theorem* and *Stokes' Theorem*, have critical applications in fluid dynamics, electricity, and magnetism. Both measure different properties accumulated over a surface compared to going around the bounding curve.

V. Green's Theorem is named after its discoverer, George Green (1793–1841).

A. George Green, who had little formal education, worked in his father's bakery for most of his life and taught himself mathematics from books.

B. He proved his famous theorem in a privately published book that he wrote to describe electricity and magnetism.

C. He did not attend college until he was 40.

D. He had seven children, all with the same woman, Jane Smith, but never married. This factor became important when he secured a position in college that required that he be unmarried!

E. He never knew the importance of his work, but it and its consequences have been described as "…leading to the mathematical theories of electricity underlying 20th-century industry."

VI. The Fundamental Theorem for Line Integrals, the Divergence Theorem (also known as Gauss's Theorem), Green's Theorem, and Stokes' Theorem are all variations of the Fundamental Theorem of Calculus.

    A. Each of these variations can be predicted to be true by understanding the philosophy of the Fundamental Theorem of Calculus in its most basic form: "Accumulated change equals net effect."

    B. People are adept at generalizing and extending ideas.

    C. Those generalizations and extensions are important.

    D. In these examples, those generalizations are central to the way we understand and describe various physical phenomena, from fluid flow to electricity and magnetism.

Readings:

Schey, H. M. *Div, Grad, Curl, and All That: An Informal Text on Vector Calculus*.

Any standard vector calculus book.

Questions to Consider:

1. Explain how surveying, together with global positioning technology, describes the meaning of the Fundamental Theorem for Line Integrals.

2. Suppose a function of three variables described the exact temperature at every point in a large volume of space. What are two ways to measure the difference in temperature from the starting point to the ending point of a path that a flying object might take in this volume? State a version of the Fundamental Theorem for Line Integrals for paths in space.

Lecture Twenty-Two
Fields of Arrows—Differential Equations

Scope: In this lecture, we introduce the idea of a *differential equation*, an equation that involves not only a function but also its derivatives. Differential equations govern numerous scientific, biological, and economic processes. The solution of a differential equation is not a number but a function or, formally speaking, a family of functions. Because algebraic solutions are rather difficult to obtain, we use a geometric approach to understand the behavior of the solutions. We will see these ideas applied to real life when we examine illustrative models of population growth and the behavior of springs and pendulums.

Outline

I. Mathematics and calculus are incredibly powerful at allowing us to understand and manipulate the world. For example, suppose we want to know how much money will be in our savings account if we deposit $1,000 today in an account that pays 5% per year compounded continuously.

   A. The rate at which the account is growing is really information about the rate of change of the function that tells us how much money is in the account at every moment. *Rate of change* means derivative.

   B. We can write down an equation that captures this information:
   $$\frac{dm}{dt} = .05\, m(t),$$ where m = money and t = time.

   C. We see that the function of the amount of money in our account will become increasingly steep as money accumulates.

   D. This equation is a differential equation. It talks about a function, in this case $m(t)$, and relates the function's values with the value of its derivative. Thus, the answer to a differential equation is not a number; it is a function.

II. Differential equations arise in applications to many areas.

A. Newton and Leibniz wrote down the first differential equations; they came about at the very dawn of calculus.

B. Differential equations have central applications in all areas of physics, as well as biology, economics, the social sciences, and basically any area you can think of.

III. Let's look at a basic example of a differential equation in physics.

A. Suppose you know from observations that a dropped object after t seconds will travel at $-32t$ feet per second.

B. You might want to know how far it has fallen after t seconds.

    1. The information given presents us with a differential equation, namely, $\dfrac{dp}{dt} = -32t$.

    2. Our challenge is to find a function $p(t)$ whose derivative is $-32t$.

    3. We know how to find such an antiderivative:

$$p(t) = -16t^2 + C$$

    (where C = the position of the ball at time 0).

C. When we have a differential equation, its solution often gives us a *family of functions*.

D. Differential equations are equations involving functions *and their derivatives*, and their solutions are not numbers but, rather, *functions*.

IV. Physics is abundant with situations modeled by differential equations.

A. For example, Newton's law, $F = ma$, is a differential equation, if we remember that acceleration is the second derivative of position.

B. If you have an *initial value problem* for a differential equation, it means you are given the initial conditions; thus, we get one solution equation instead of a family of equations.

C. Often when we are dealing with differential equations, we may want to model some particular behavior. In this case, we refine the model and add more conditions to make it more realistic.

D. For example, when we drop an object in the air, we need to account for air resistance, which is proportional to the velocity.

Therefore, the more accurate equation for measuring the speed of a falling body becomes: $m\dfrac{d^2p}{dt^2} = -32m + cm\dfrac{dp}{dt}$, that is, the force, and hence acceleration, is a function of time, position, and velocity!

E. Another physical situation that is modeled by a differential equation is that of the pendulum, if we wish to know what the angle is at each time.

F. For a spring of mass m stretched a distance x from equilibrium, Hooke's Law asserts that the force is kx. Thus, the differential equation is $m\dfrac{d^2x}{dt^2} = -kx$.

V. As we see, differential equations involve discovering that a certain physical process is governed by a differential equation, then finding a method to solve that equation. Many mathematicians contributed to the growth of this field in the 17th and 18th centuries.

A. Newton and Leibniz, having invented the notion of derivatives, were the first to write down differential equations.

B. The Bernoulli brothers, Jakob and Johann, and Johann's son, Daniel, solved many problems in mechanics and applied differential equations to complex physics problems, such as fluid dynamics. Their jealous and quarrelsome nature did not deter progress in calculus in the late 17th and early 18th centuries.

C. Significant contributions toward algebraic solutions of differential equations were developed by Joseph Louis Lagrange, whose 1788 work *Méchanique Analytique* is an elegant and comprehensive treatise on Newtonian mechanics.

D. Another important contributor to the solutions of differential equations was Pierre Simon de Laplace, an expert in celestial mechanics; his method of transforming differential equations into algebraic ones, the *Laplace Transform*, is a key tool in solving differential equations, even today.

VI. We can use differential equations and direction fields to study population dynamics.

A. The simplest model, attributable to British economist Thomas Malthus in 1798, is the exponential growth model that we have already seen: $\dfrac{dy}{dt} = ry$, where r is the growth rate and y is the population.

B. The problem with Malthus's model is that it assumes an infinite supply of resources. Because resources are limited, the population cannot grow forever.

VII. Before we continue, we need to look at a simple geometric approach to solving such a differential equation without finding a formula for the solution.

    A. We consider an entire plane viewed as having a horizontal time axis (t) and a vertical population axis (y).

    B. Although we don't know what the function is that satisfies the differential equation, we do know that the derivative of the function y is some constant r times the value of the function, and we know that the derivative is the slope of the tangent line.

    C. Thus, to obtain a direction field, at each point (t, y), we draw a little arrow that captures the slope of the tangent line.

    D. Then, if we start at a given point, that is, at some initial condition, we simply follow the arrows to trace out our function.

VIII. An alternative to Malthus's model is the *logistic model*, or *Verhulst model*.

    A. Once the population reaches the saturation level, or carrying capacity K, it requires too many resources and begins to decline. This means that for $y > K$, $\dfrac{dy}{dt} < 0$.

    B. The differential equation is: $\dfrac{dy}{dt} = ry\left(1 - \dfrac{y}{K}\right)$.

    C. Notice that for small y, we essentially have exponential growth, and for $y > K$, $\dfrac{dy}{dt}$ is negative, as needed.

D. When we look at the direction field, we notice that no matter what the initial condition is, as time goes on, all solutions approach the carrying capacity K.

IX. Another alternative to Malthus's model is the *critical threshold model.*

   A. We assume that unless the population is above some critical threshold T, it cannot grow at all. For example, if you don't have enough people in the population, the population will not grow! This means that for $y < T$, $\dfrac{dy}{dt} < 0$.

   B. The differential equation is: $\dfrac{dy}{dt} = ry\left(1 - \dfrac{T}{y}\right)$.

   C. We can put together the two models.

   1. The combined model satisfies both assumptions: that there is a minimum threshold for population growth and limited resources.
   2. The direction field shows that if the initial population is less than T, then as time goes on, it declines to zero. Otherwise, it approaches the carrying capacity K.
   3. We can use computers to put in as many points in the direction field as we wish to get very accurate estimations of the actual answer.

   D. A variation of this model describes the passenger pigeon population in the United States. The pigeons had a very high critical threshold T, so when they were hunted down to such small numbers in the late 1800s, the population could no longer grow, and they became extinct in 1914.

X. Differential equations also appear in a variety of other contexts, including the spread of epidemics, hormone balance, chemical reactions, and planetary motion.

Readings:

Any standard calculus textbook, chapters on differential equations. For population dynamics, see Boyce and DiPrima, *Elementary Differential Equations and Boundary Value Problems*, 8th ed., Section 2.6.

Questions to Consider:

1. In the Verhulst model, at what population level is the population growing fastest?

2. In a fishery, a fraction E of the population is culled every year. Assuming the Verhulst model, what would be the differential equation for this fishery? If $E > r$, what is the long-term behavior? If $E < r$, what is the long-term behavior?

Lecture Twenty-Three
Owls, Rats, Waves, and Guitars

Scope: In this lecture, our ideas extend to contexts involving many variables, such as multiple-species populations and the analysis of vibrating strings. Is a decade-long decrease in the population of the Pacific owl a result of the predator-prey relationships in the forest or human intervention? Differential equations can help us understand what to expect about the behavior of populations when more than one species is interacting. When we turn our attention to music, we find the analysis of waves in a vibrating string to be another rich application area for differential equations. In this case, the equations we seek involve more than one variable.

Outline

I. We have seen that differential equations describe physical and biological phenomena.

    A. We have been primarily interested in functions of one variable, namely time.

    B. We have also seen that we can understand solutions of differential equations geometrically without knowing the exact algebraic form.

    C. Most physical phenomena include more than one variable, and the topic of this lecture is differential equations in several variables.

II. Once again, we will attempt to develop a mathematical model that describes population dynamics, but in this case, we have two species involved that are related to one another in a predator-prey relationship.

    A. In the northern California redwoods, the woodrat provides 80% of the food for the spotted owl, which is the main predator of the woodrat.

    B. Let $w(t)$ be the population of the woodrat and $s(t)$ be the population of the spotted owl as functions of time.

C. If there are no owls, that is, $y = 0$, we assume that the population of the woodrat grows exponentially: $\dfrac{dw}{dt} = w$.

D. Similarly, if the are no woodrats, that is, $w = 0$, we assume that the owls die out exponentially with rate $r = 0.75$: $\dfrac{ds}{dt} = -0.75s$. (We use 0.75 for the purpose of illustration.)

E. Whenever an owl and a woodrat meet, we assume that there is some chance that the owl eats a woodrat, hence survives and is able to reproduce, resulting in an increase of the owl population and a decrease in the woodrat population.

F. Thus, the *system* of differential equations becomes the following:

$$\frac{dw}{dt} = w - 0.5ws$$

$$\frac{ds}{dt} = -0.75s + 0.25ws$$

G. How do we analyze such a system? Consider the direction field approach again.

    1. At each point (w,s), regardless of t, we know the rates of change $\dfrac{dw}{dt}$ and $\dfrac{ds}{dt}$.

    2. Thus, we know the rate of change of $\dfrac{dw}{ds}$, as well, and we draw an arrow in the direction $\left(\dfrac{ds}{dt}, \dfrac{dw}{dt} \right)$.

    3. Then, if we start at a given point, that is, at some initial condition (w,s), we simply follow the arrows to trace out the evolution of w and s as functions of t.

H. In this system, we observe a cyclical nature for the populations of the woodrat and the spotted owl.

1. Notice first that the populations are constant exactly when $\dfrac{dw}{dt} = 0$ and $\dfrac{ds}{dt} = 0$. This occurs at (0,0) and (3,2). The population is stable at these points.

2. Otherwise, if we start at another point such as (3.5,1), as the population of the woodrat increases, so does the population of the spotted owl.

3. Eventually, the population of the woodrat decreases, and this results in a decrease in the population of the spotted owl. This, in turn, fuels the growth of the population of the woodrat, and we are back to the beginning of the cycle.

4. With different initial conditions, for example, (2,1.25), we see a different curved pattern.

I. These models for predator-prey relationships were pioneered by American biophysicist Alfred Lotka and Italian mathematician Vito Volterra in the early 20th century.

   1. They have been verified in several examples, including by the records of the Hudson Bay Company of Canada, which traded lynx and snowshoe hare pelts in 1845–1935.

   2. In these examples, the cyclical nature with a period of 9–10 years is distinctly pronounced.

III. Now we look at an example of differential equations that model the behavior of a vibrating string, the *wave equation*. In this case, we will find that we are seeking a function of two variables.

A. Consider an elastic string of length L tightly stretched between two supports at the same horizontal level, for example, a guitar string.

B. Now, pluck the string and let it vibrate freely.

C. To describe the behavior of the string, we are interested in how each point on the string moves. That movement is captured by a function of two variables: the position along the string, x, and the time, t.

D. At each such position x and time t, we are interested in the vertical displacement $u(x, t)$ of the string.

E. What do we know about a vibrating string that would allow us to figure out the function $u(x, t)$ that would capture the string's motion?

F. If the string is exactly straight, no force is causing it to rise.

G. But we imagine that the string is moving and we see what forces are acting on each piece of string. The forces are those that come from the tension of the string. Newton's famous law, $F = ma$, tells us how the forces pulling on a point of the string impel that point to accelerate.

H. The derivation of the wave equation involves drawing pictures of a piece of the string and resolving the forces that are pulling at angles to tell us how the string is accelerating.

I. We find that the wave equation is:

$$\frac{\partial^2 u(x,t)}{\partial t^2} = c^2 \frac{\partial^2 u(x,t)}{\partial x^2}.$$

J. These equations mean that the acceleration of a point on the string at a fixed point x as time varies is proportional to the acceleration of the height with respect to the position along the string.

K. If we attempt to describe the vibration of a guitar string or a violin string, we have additional constraints, namely, the string is fixed at the endpoints of the string and we assume that the string is displaced in a certain way to start the vibration. That is, the string is plucked (imagine its being put into a shape and then released at time $t = 0$).

L. The solutions of the wave equations involve the sine function. This function is periodic, as we would expect. We can look at the solutions to the wave equation and see how the behavior of the string can be thought of as a sum of sine curves that corresponds to integer divisions of the total length of the string.

M. Therefore, every integer fraction of the length of the string will give a different rate of vibration; thus, the actual notes of the string can be viewed as a combination of those sine-like functions that contribute higher pitches. We have a combination where the string will naturally vibrate up and down like a sine curve at all times;

then inside it, we have the more refined numbers of vibrations. That is why the notes we hear from a guitar are so rich sounding.

Readings:

Any standard differential equations book on partial differential equations and systems of differential equations.

Questions to Consider:

1. What are some of the pitfalls of relying entirely on mathematical models for setting environmental (or other) policy?

2. The solutions to the wave equation for a string of length π have a factor of $\sin(k\pi x)$, where x gives the position on the string and k is a positive integer. Verify that this $\sin(k\pi x)$ term corresponds to having $(k-1)$ equally spaced points along the string, besides the endpoints, where the string does not move up and down at all. This result was physically demonstrated in the lecture using a guitar string.

Lecture Twenty-Four
Calculus Everywhere

Scope: Calculus is effective in dealing with quantities that are varying smoothly. Although there are limits to the realms of applicability of calculus, it would be difficult to exaggerate its importance and influence on our real lives. Calculus is so effective because it is a tool for quantitatively studying change and how parts combine to create the whole. The techniques and strategies of calculus all arise from two fundamental ideas—the derivative and the integral— each motivated by straightforward observations of everyday occurrences. It took thousands of years to develop these ideas, but there is still much more to come in calculus and beyond, for calculus continues to be one of the most fruitful and influential strategies for analyzing our world that has ever been devised.

Outline

I. Calculus is so effective because it is a tool for quantitatively studying change and how parts combine to create the whole.

    A. The techniques and strategies of calculus all arise from two fundamental ideas—the derivative and the integral.

    B. Further extensions of the ideas of calculus and further applications of these ideas are actively pursued to this day.

II. We have touched the wealth of ideas related to calculus, and each idea is the tip of the iceberg.

    A. For example, we started the course by considering the motion of a car and developing the two fundamental ideas of calculus, the derivative and the integral, in that context.

    B. But calculus is also extensively used in the inner workings of the car: the physical motion of the engine pistons, the optimization problem for optimal fuel consumption, and the differential equations guiding the heating and cooling systems.

    C. Likewise, the heat equation not only helps us to understand the way heat moves in the engine, but its variations are among the tools used in the analysis of the pricing of financial derivatives.

D. As well, electric circuits are described by differential equations.

III. Let's remember some of the concepts we have covered in the course and how we could have expanded those concepts.

    A. We considered the problem of hydrostatic force acting on a dam. But we could have talked about any number of other optimization problems involving power generation at a dam.

    B. We have also seen how calculus helps determine optimal architectural structures, such as suspension bridges and arches.

    C. We saw an example of using calculus as part of product design when we studied how calculus helps us design soda cans that minimize the amount of aluminum used. The same optimization techniques are used to design rockets that put telecommunications satellites in orbit.

        1. The rocket consists of several propulsion stages with the satellite on top. Each stage accelerates the rocket by burning fuel. Once a stage burns all its fuel, it is simply jettisoned, and the next stage is activated.

        2. Calculus is used to minimize the mass of the rocket while achieving the desired velocity.

IV. The potency of calculus is a testament to the power of abstraction.

    A. We have seen repeatedly that the methods of solving problems in a bewildering array of fields magically involve the same processes that are captured in the derivative, the integral, and the limit.

    B. We can view even apparently static objects as dynamically growing or changing. This perspective allows us to analyze them in a different and often effective way.

    C. The habit of recasting a problem to see it dynamically creates new insights.

    D. Calculus gives us specific tools and an underlying philosophy about how to view and interpret the world. It gives a perspective that can be applied or attempted in many settings.

    E. Often, looking at an issue from the calculus point of view can lead to productive insights.

V. From one point of view, the story of calculus is the story of the intellectual conquest of infinity.

A. The derivative and the integral are the two fundamental ideas of calculus.

B. We saw them arise through a commonsensical analysis of the everyday phenomenon of motion—a car on a straight road.

C. But the derivative and the integral were processes that had amazingly rich structures.

D. The definition of the derivative arose from the analysis of the car moving on a straight road, studying the average velocity of the car in increasingly small increments of time. The derivative is the limit of those average velocities as Δt goes to 0.

E. The integral is a sum. It allowed us to add up little pieces—thin sections of areas or slices of volumes to create the whole from its parts.

F. We also talked about infinite series, which is a way of taking a complicated function and dealing with it as a simple function. The sine function, for example, can be viewed as an infinite polynomial.

G. In the last two lectures, we talked about direction fields as solutions to differential equations. If we imagine the arrows being more and more numerous, to infinity, we could find a smooth solution to a differential equation.

VI. One of the geometric views of calculus was that if you magnified a graph of a differential function closely, it would look like a straight line. Likewise, if you have a function of two variables that is differentiable, it will look like a flat plane.

A. In the 19th century, however, mathematicians Weierstrass and Bolzano both showed a function that was continuous but not differentiable. It was not smooth at all.

B. In the world of fractals, the Koch Curve uses an infinite process to produce a curve that is not smooth-looking when viewed arbitrarily closely.

C. The Devil's Staircase is an example of a graph of a perfectly continuous function that is flat almost everywhere. This is another example of applying the idea of infinity to different situations.

VII. There is much more to come in calculus and beyond.

A. Thousands of papers are written about calculus today, and hundreds of thousands of papers in engineering, physics, biology, and other arenas use calculus.

B. Newton said, "If I have seen farther than others, it is because I have stood on the shoulders of giants." In exploring calculus, we have stood on Newton's shoulders, on Leibniz's shoulders, on Archimedes's shoulders, and those of many other great thinkers. We have communed with some truly spectacular highpoints of human thought. All of us can share an appreciation for that giant conceptual development that shaped and continues to shape history—calculus.

Readings:

Any standard calculus textbook with applications.

Boyer, Carl B. *The History of the Calculus and Its Conceptual Development.*

Questions to Consider:

1. What intellectual developments in history compare to calculus in their influence?

2. To what realms of the world is mathematical analysis appropriate or not appropriate? How has the answer to that question changed over time?

Timeline

All dates are approximate in the sense that the mathematical activities mentioned each spanned several or many years.

540 B.C. .... Pythagoras founded his school and proved the Pythagorean Theorem.

450 B.C. .... Zeno posed his paradoxes of motion.

355 B.C. .... Eudoxus was associated with the method of exhaustion that was an integral-like process.

300 B.C. .... Euclid presented the axiomatic method in geometry in his *Elements*.

225 B.C. .... Archimedes used integral-like procedures to find formulas for various areas and volumes of geometrical figures.

225 B.C. .... Apollonius described the geometry of conic sections.

A.D. 1545 .... Tartaglia, Cardano, and Ferrari were involved with the algebraic solution of cubic and quartic equations.

1600 .... Kepler and Galileo did work on motion and planetary motion, describing those mathematically.

1629 .... Fermat developed methods of finding *maxima* and *minima* using infinitesimal methods resembling the derivative.

1635 .... Cavalieri developed a method of indivisibles.

1650 .... Descartes developed connections between geometry and algebra and invented methods for finding tangents to curves.

1665–1666	During these plague years, Newton devised calculus, his laws of motion, the universal law of gravitation, and works on optics.
1669	Barrow formulated ideas leading to the Fundamental Theorem of Calculus and resigned his chair at Cambridge in favor of Newton.
1672	Leibniz independently discovered calculus and devised notation commonly used now.
1700	The Bernoullis were involved with the development and application of calculus on the continent.
1715	Brook Taylor and Colin Maclaurin developed ideas of approximating functions by infinite series.
1750	Euler developed a tremendous amount of mathematics, including applications and extensions of calculus, especially infinite series.
1788	Lagrange developed ideas about infinite series and the calculus of variations.
1805	Laplace worked on partial differential equations and applications of calculus to probability theory.
1822	Fourier invented a method of approximating functions using trigonometric series.
1827	Cauchy developed ideas in infinite series and complex variable theory and refined the definitions of limit and continuity.

1851 .... Riemann developed a modern definition of the integral.

1854 .... Weierstrass formulated the rigorous definition of the limit used today.

1700–present day .... Innumerable mathematicians, scientists, engineers, and others have applied calculus to all areas of mathematics, science, economics, technology, and many other fields. Mathematicians continue to develop new mathematics based on the ideas of calculus.

Glossary

Acceleration: Rate of change of velocity; a measure of how fast the velocity is changing. The second derivative of position. Units are distance/time^2.

Antiderivative (of a function f): A function with a derivative equal to f.

Brachistochrone: A curve traced between two points (not atop one another), along which a freely falling object will reach the bottom point in the least amount of time.

Continuous function: A function that has no breaks or gaps in its graph; the graph of a continuous function can be drawn without lifting the pen.

Cosine: A function of angle θ giving the ratio of the length of the adjacent side to the length of the hypotenuse of a right triangle, as well as the horizontal coordinate of a point on the circle of radius 1 corresponding to the angle θ.

Delta (Δ): The Greek letter capital delta is used in such expressions as Δt or Δx to denote a small change in the varying quantity. We should think of the Δ as shorthand for "difference." In the definition of the integral, Δx or Δt appears in the long sums used to define the integral. The Δ is transformed into a dx or dt in the integral symbol to remind us of the origins of the integral as a sum.

Derivative: Mathematical description of (instantaneous) rate of change of a function. Characterized geometrically as the slope of the tangent line to the graph of the function. The derivative of a function $f(x)$ is written

$f'(x)$ or $\dfrac{d}{dx}(f(x))$ and is formally defined as

$\lim\limits_{\Delta x \to 0} \dfrac{f(x + \Delta x) - f(x)}{\Delta x}$.

Differentiable function: A function whose derivative exists at every point where the function is defined; a continuous function without kinks or cusps.

Differential equation: An equation involving a function and its derivatives; a solution of a differential equation is a family of functions.

Directional derivative: The rate of change of a function of several variables in the direction of a given vector.

Direction field: A two-dimensional field of arrows indicating the slope of the tangent line at each given point for a curve that is a solution of a differential equation.

Epicycles: A circle on a circle. For centuries before Kepler, people believed that planets' orbits were circular, but because that image did not accord with observation, the planets were viewed as revolving around on little circles whose centers were going in circles. The smaller circles with centers on circles are epicycles.

Exhaustion (the Greek method of exhaustion): A geometric technique by which formulas for areas of different shapes could be verified through finer and finer approximations.

Fourier Series: An infinite series of sines and cosines, typically used to approximate a function.

Function: Mathematical description of dependency. A rule or correspondence that provides exactly one output value for each input value. Often written algebraically as $f(x)$ = formula involving x (for example, $f(x) = x^2$).

Fundamental Theorem of Calculus: The most important theorem in calculus. Demonstrates the reciprocal relationship between the derivative and the integral.

Graph: A geometric representation of a function, showing correspondences via pairs of points (input, output) drawn on a standard Cartesian (x-y) plane.

Heat equation: A partial differential equation governing the heating and cooling of objects; it relates the second derivative of position to the first derivative of time.

Infinite series (also called an infinite sum): The sum of an infinite collection of numbers. Such a series can sum to a finite number or "diverge to infinity"; for example, $\frac{1}{2} + \frac{1}{4} + \frac{1}{8} + \frac{1}{16} + \ldots$ sums to 1, but $1 + \frac{1}{2} + \frac{1}{3} + \frac{1}{4} + \ldots$ does not sum to a finite number.

Integer: A whole number (positive, zero, or negative); …–2, –1, 0, 1, 2,…

Integral: Denoted $\int_a^b v(t)dt$. If we think of function $v(t)$ as measuring the velocity of a moving car at each time t, then the integral is a number that is equal to the distance traveled, because the integral is obtained by dividing the time from a to b into small increments and approximating the distance traveled by assuming that the car went at a steady speed during each of those small increments of time. By taking increasingly smaller increments of time, approximations converge to a single answer, the integral. This sounds complicated, but the naturality of it is the topic of Lecture Three. The integral is also equal to the area under the graph of $v(t)$ and above the t-axis. The integral is related to the derivative (as an inverse procedure) via the Fundamental Theorem of Calculus. See also **antiderivative**.

Law of Large Numbers: The theorem that the ratio of successes to trials in a random process will converge to the probability of success as increasingly many trials are undertaken.

Limit: The result of an infinite process that converges to a single answer. Example: the sequence of numbers $1, \frac{1}{2}, \frac{1}{3}, \frac{1}{4}, \frac{1}{5}, \ldots$ converges to the number 0.

Maximum: The largest value of the outputs of a function. The y-value of the highest point on the graph of a function. It does not always exist.

Minimum: The smallest value of the outputs of a function. The y-value of the lowest point on the graph of a function. It does not always exist.

Newton-Raphson Method: An iterative technique for finding solutions of an equation using graphs and derivatives.

Parabola: A conic section defined as the set of all points equidistant between a point and a line.

Paradox: Two compelling arguments about the same situation that lead to two opposite views. Zeno's paradoxes of motion give logical reasons why motion cannot occur. On the other hand, we experience motion. The opposite conclusions deduced from Zeno's logic versus our experience compose the paradox.

Partial derivative: The rate of change of a quantity relative to the change of one of several quantities that are influencing its value when the other varying quantities remain fixed.

Partial differential equation: An equation involving a function of several variables and its partial derivatives.

π (pi): Greek letter denoting the value 3.1415926… equal to the ratio of the circumference of a circle to its diameter.

Probability: The quantitative study of uncertainty.

Real number: Any decimal number.

Sine: A function of angle θ giving the ratio of the length of the opposite side to the length of the hypotenuse of a right triangle, as well as the vertical coordinate of a point on the circle of radius 1 corresponding to the angle θ.

Slope (of a straight line): The ratio of distance ascended to distance traversed, sometimes known as "rise over run."

Smooth function: A function that is continuous and whose first derivative, second derivative, and so forth are all continuous.

Tangent line: A straight line associated to each point on a curve. Just grazing the curve, the tangent line "parallels" the curve at a point.

Variable: The independent quantity in a functional relationship. For example, if position is a function of time, time is the variable.

Vector: An arrow indicating direction and magnitude (usually of motion in two-dimensional or three-dimensional space).

Vector field: A field of arrows associating a vector to each point (x,y) in the two-dimensional plane; usually represented graphically.

Velocity: Average velocity is total distance divided by the time it took to traverse that distance; units are length/time (for example, miles per hour). Instantaneous velocity is the speed at one moment of time, approximated by average velocity for smaller and smaller time intervals; units are also length/time. The instantaneous velocity is the derivative of the position function for a moving object.

Wave equation: A partial differential equation governing the displacement of a string as well as more complex phenomena, such as electromagnetic waves; it relates the second derivative of position to the second derivative of time.

Biographical Notes

Archimedes (c. 287–212 B.C.). Ancient Greek mathematician, physicist, astronomer, inventor, and prolific author of scientific treatises. He studied hydrostatics and mechanics and discovered the general principle of the lever, how to compute tangents to spirals, the volume and surface area of spheres, the volume of solids of revolution, many applications of the method of exhaustion, and an approximation of the value of π, among other work. Archimedes was killed by a Roman soldier when Syracuse was conquered during the Second Punic War.

Barrow, Isaac (1630–1677). Lucasian professor of mathematics at Cambridge. In 1669, Barrow resigned from his chair to give Newton the professorship. He contributed to the development of integral calculus, particularly through the recognition of its inverse relationship with the tangent. He published works in optics and geometry and edited the works of ancient Greek mathematicians, including Euclid and Archimedes.

Bernoulli, Daniel (1700–1782). Swiss professor of mathematics at St. Petersburg and at Basel. He is best known for work in fluid dynamics (the *Bernoulli principle* is named for him) and is also known for work in probability. He was the son of Jean Bernoulli.

Bernoulli, Jacques (often called Jakob or James) (1654–1705). Professor of mathematics at Basel and a student of Leibniz. He studied infinite series and was the first to publish on the use of polar coordinates (the *lemniscate of Bernoulli* is named for him). He formulated the Law of Large Numbers in probability theory and wrote an influential treatise on the subject. Together, Jacques and brother Jean were primarily responsible for disseminating Leibniz's calculus throughout Europe.

Bernoulli, Jean (often called Johannes or John) (1667–1748). Swiss mathematician. He was professor of mathematics at Groningen (Holland) and Basel (after the death of his brother Jacques). He was a student of Leibniz and applied techniques of calculus to many problems in geometry and mechanics. He proposed the famous Brachistochrone problem as a challenge to other mathematicians. Jean Bernoulli was the teacher of Euler and L'Hôpital (who provided Jean a regular salary in return for mathematical discoveries, including the well-known *L'Hôpital's Rule*).

Buffon, Georges Louis Leclerc, Comte de (1707–1788). French naturalist and author of *Histoire naturelle*. He translated Newton's *Method of Fluxions* into French. He formulated the Buffon's Needle problem, linking the study of probability to geometric techniques.

Cauchy, Augustin Louis (1789–1857). Prolific French mathematician and engineer. He was professor in the Ecole Polytechnique and professor of mathematical physics at Turin. He worked in number theory, algebra, astronomy, mechanics, optics, and elasticity theory and made great contributions to analysis (particularly the study of infinite series and of complex variable theory) and the calculus of variations. He improved the foundations of calculus by refining the definitions of limit and continuity.

Cavalieri, Bonaventura (1598–1647). Italian mathematician; professor at Bologna; student of Galileo. He developed the method of indivisibles that provided a transition between the Greek method of exhaustion and the modern methods of integration of Newton and Leibniz. He applied his method to solve a majority of the problems posed by Kepler.

Descartes, René (1596–1650). French mathematician and philosopher. He served in various military campaigns and tutored Princess Elizabeth (daughter of Frederick V) and Queen Christina of Sweden. Descartes developed crucial theoretical links between algebra and geometry and his own method of constructing tangents to curves. He made substantial contributions to the development of analytic geometry.

Euler, Leonhard (1707–1783). Swiss mathematician and scientist. Euler was the student of Jean Bernoulli. He was professor of medicine and physiology and later became a professor of mathematics at St. Petersburg. Euler is the most prolific mathematical author of all time, writing on mathematics, acoustics, engineering, mechanics, and astronomy. He introduced standardized notations, many now in modern use, and contributed unique ideas to all areas of analysis, especially in the study of infinite series. He lost nearly all his sight by 1771 and was the father of 13 children.

Fermat, Pierre de (1601–1665). French lawyer and judge in Toulouse; enormously talented amateur mathematician. Fermat worked in number theory, geometry, analysis, and algebra and was the first developer of analytic geometry, including the discovery of equations of lines, circles, ellipses, parabolas, and hyperbolas. He wrote *Introduction to Plane and*

Solid Loci and formulated the famed *Fermat's Last Theorem* as a note in the margin of his copy of Bachet's *Diophantus*. He developed a procedure for finding maxima and minima of functions through infinitesimal analysis, essentially by the limit definition of derivative, and applied this technique to many problems, including analyzing the refraction of light.

Fourier, Jean Baptiste Joseph (1768–1830). French mathematical physicist and professor in the Ecole Polytechnique. Fourier accompanied Napoleon on his campaign to Egypt, was appointed secretary of Napoleon's Institute of Egypt, and served as prefect of Grenoble. He carried out extensive studies in heat propagation, which form the foundation of modern partial differential equations with boundary conditions. He developed the *Fourier Series*, which represents functions by infinite (trigonometric) series.

Galilei, Galileo (1564–1642). Italian mathematician and philosopher; professor of mathematics at Pisa and at Padua. He invented the telescope (after hearing of such a device) and made many astronomical discoveries, including the existence of the rings of Saturn. He established the first law of motion, laws of falling bodies, and the fact that projectiles move in parabolic curves. Galileo made great contributions to the study of dynamics, leading to consideration of infinitesimals (eventually formalized in the theory of calculus). He advocated the Copernican heliocentric model of the solar system and was subsequently placed under house arrest by the Inquisition.

Gauss, Carl Friedrich (1777–1855). German mathematician; commonly considered the world's greatest mathematician, hence known as the Prince of Mathematicians. He was professor of astronomy and director of the observatory at Göttingen. Gauss provided the first complete proof of the Fundamental Theorem of Algebra and made substantial contributions to geometry, algebra, number theory, and applied mathematics. He established mathematical rigor as the standard of proof. His work on the differential geometry of curved surfaces formed an essential base for Einstein's general theory of relativity.

Green, George (1793–1841). Most famous for his theorem known as *Green's Theorem*. He worked in his father's bakery for most of his life and taught himself mathematics from books. He proved his famous theorem in a privately published book that he wrote to describe electricity and magnetism. Green did not attend college until he was 40. He had seven children (all with the same woman, Jane Smith) but never married. He never knew the importance of his work, but it and its consequences have been described as "…leading to the mathematical theories of electricity underlying 20th-century industry."

Kepler, Johannes (1571–1630). German astronomer and mathematician; mathematician and astrologer to Emperor Rudolph II (in Prague). Kepler assisted Tycho Brahe (the Danish astronomer) in compiling the best collection of astronomical observations in the pre-telescope era. He developed three laws of planetary motion and made the first attempt to justify them mathematically. They were later shown to be a consequence of the universal law of gravitation by Newton, applying the new techniques of calculus.

Lagrange, Joseph Louis (1736–1813). French mathematician; professor at the Royal Artillery School in Turin, at the Ecole Normale and the Ecole Polytechnique in France, and at the Berlin Academy of Sciences. He studied algebra, number theory, and differential equations and unified the theory of general mechanics. He developed classical results in the theory of infinite series and contributed to the analytical foundation of the calculus of variations.

Laplace, Pierre Simon de (1749–1827). French mathematician and astronomer; professor at the Ecole Normale and the Ecole Polytechnique. Laplace was the author of the influential *Mécanique Céleste* that summarized all contributions to the theory of gravitation (without credit to its contributors). He developed potential theory, important in the study of physics, and partial differential equations. He made great contributions to probability theory based on techniques from calculus.

Leibniz, Gottfried Wilhelm von (1646–1716). German diplomat, logician, politician, philosopher, linguist, and mathematician; president of the Berlin Academy. Leibniz is regarded, with Newton, as a co-inventor of calculus. He was the first to publish a theory of calculus. Leibniz's notation is used currently. He made substantial contributions to formal logic, leading to the establishment of symbolic logic as a field of study. He discovered an infinite series formula for $\dfrac{\pi}{4}$. He was accused of plagiarism by British partisans of Newton, and his supporters counterclaimed that Newton was the plagiarist. Now, he is acknowledged to have independently discovered calculus.

L'Hôpital, Guillaume François Antoine (1661–1704). French marquis, amateur mathematician, and student of Jean Bernoulli. L'Hôpital provided one of the five submitted solutions to Bernoulli's Brachistochrone problem. He was the author of the first calculus textbook (1696), written in the vernacular and based primarily on the work of Jean Bernoulli. This text went through several editions and greatly aided the spread of Leibniz's calculus on the Continent.

Lotka, Alfred J. (1880–1949). An American biophysicist and the father of mathematical biology; he published the first book in this field in 1924. With Vito Volterra, he is chiefly known for the formulation of the Lotka-Volterra equations for the study of predator-prey models in population dynamics.

Newton, Sir Isaac (1642–1727). Great English mathematician and scientist; Lucasian professor of mathematics at Cambridge. Newton was the first discoverer of differential and integral calculus. He formulated the law of universal gravitation and his three laws of motion, upon which classical physics is based. In 1687, he published his results in *Philosophiae Naturalis Principia Mathematica*. He formulated the theory of colors (in optics) and proved the binomial theorem. He is possibly the greatest genius of all time. Newton was a Member of Parliament (Cambridge), long-time president of the Royal Society, and Master of the Mint. The controversy with Leibniz over attribution of the discovery of calculus poisoned relations between British and Continental scientists, leading to the isolation of British mathematicians for much of the 18th century.

Riemann, Georg Friedrich Bernhard (1826–1866). German mathematician; professor of mathematics at Göttingen. He made great contributions to analysis, geometry, and number theory and both extended the theory of representing a function by its Fourier series and established the foundations of complex variable theory. Riemann developed the concept and theory of the Riemann integral (as taught in standard college calculus courses) and pioneered the study of the theory of functions of a real variable. He gave the most famous job talk in the history of mathematics, in which he provided a mathematical generalization of all known geometries, a field now called Riemannian geometry.

Weierstrass, Karl (1815–1897). German mathematician. He left the University of Bonn without a degree and taught secondary school for more than 12 years while independently studying analysis. His 1854 paper led to a professorship in Berlin. He provided a rigorous definition of the limit, thus placing calculus at last on solid mathematical ground, and he provided a precise definition of real numbers.

Zeno of Elea (c. 495–430 B.C.). Ancient Greek dialectician and logician. He is noted for his four paradoxes of motion. He was a student of Parmenides, whose school of philosophy rivaled that of the Pythagoreans.

Bibliography

Readings

Bardi, Jason Socrates. *The Calculus Wars: Newton, Leibniz, and the Greatest Mathematical Clash of All Time*. New York: Thunder's Mouth Press, 2006. This book tells the story of the controversy between Newton and Leibniz and their supporters over who should receive credit for the discovery or invention of calculus. The fact that a book on this topic for the general reader is published in 2006 is a testament to both the significance of calculus and the level of rancor of the dispute.

Bell, E. T. *Men of Mathematics*. New York: Simon & Schuster, 1937. A classic of mathematics history, filled with quotes and stories (often apocryphal) of famous mathematicians.

Berlinski, David. *A Tour of the Calculus*. New York: Pantheon Books, 1995. This book is written in a flowery manner and gives the nonmathematician a journey through the ideas of calculus.

Blatner, David. *The Joy of π*. New York: Walker Publishing Company, 1997. This fun little paperback is filled with gems and details about the history of the irrational number π.

Boyer, Carl B. *The History of the Calculus and Its Conceptual Development*. Mineola, NY: Dover Publications, 1959. A scholarly history of calculus from ancient times through the 19th century.

―――. *A History of Mathematics*. Princeton: Princeton University Press, 1968. An extensive survey of the history of mathematics from earliest recorded history through the early 20th century. Each chapter includes a good bibliography and nice exercises.

Burger, Edward B., and Michael Starbird. *The Heart of Mathematics: An invitation to effective thinking*. Emeryville, CA: Key College Publishing, 2000. This award-winning book presents deep and fascinating mathematical ideas in a lively, accessible, and readable way. The review in the June–July 2001 issue of the *American Mathematical Monthly* says, "This is very possibly the best 'mathematics for the non-mathematician' book that I have seen—and that includes popular (non-textbook) books that one would find in a general bookstore."

―――. *Coincidences, Chaos, and All That Math Jazz: Making Light of Weighty Ideas*. New York: W.W. Norton & Co., 2005. This book fuses a professor's understanding of rigorous mathematical ideas with the distorted sensibility of a stand-up comedian. It covers many beautiful topics in mathematics that are only touched on in this course, such as probability, chaos, and infinity. "Informative, intelligent, and refreshingly irreverent," in the words of author Ian Stewart.

Cajori, Florian. *A History of Mathematics*, 5th ed. New York: Chelsea Publishing Co., 1991 (1st ed., 1893). A survey of the development of mathematics and the lives of mathematicians from ancient times through the end of World War I.

―――. "History of Zeno's Arguments on Motion." *American Mathematical Monthly*. Vol. 22, Nos. 1–9 (1915). Cajori presents a philosophical and mathematical discussion of the meaning of Zeno's four paradoxes of motion.

Calinger, Ronald. *A Contextual History of Mathematics*. Upper Saddle River, NJ: Prentice-Hall, 1999. This modern, readable text offers a survey of mathematics from the origin of numbers through the development of calculus and classical probability. It includes a nice section on the Bernoulli brothers.

Churchill, Winston Spencer. *My Early Life: A Roving Commission* (available through out-of-print bookstores only). Winston Churchill won the Nobel Prize in literature. The writing in this autobiography of his early life is absolutely delightful. We refer to only a few pages about his struggles with mathematics, but the whole book is a joy.

Davis, Donald M. *The Nature and Power of Mathematics*. Princeton: Princeton University Press, 1993. This wide-ranging book does not study the history of calculus in particular; rather, it describes an array of ideas from all areas of mathematics. It includes brief biographies of Gauss and Kepler, among other mathematicians.

Dunham, William. *Journey through Genius: The Great Theorems of Mathematics*. New York: John Wiley & Sons, 1990. Each of this book's 12 chapters covers a great idea or theorem and includes a brief history of the mathematicians who worked on that idea. Mathematicians discussed include Archimedes, Newton, the Bernoullis, and Euler.

Eves, Howard. *Great Moments in Mathematics (after 1650)*. Washington, DC: The Mathematical Association of America, 1981. This collection of lectures includes four entertaining chapters relevant to the development of calculus. These begin with the invention of differential calculus and conclude with a discussion of Fourier series.

Goodstein, David L., Judith R. Goodstein, and R. P. Feynman, *Feynman's Lost Lecture: The Motion of Planets around the Sun*. New York: W.W. Norton & Co., 1996. This book and CD give Feynman's geometric explanation for elliptical orbits of planets, as well as a history of the problem from Copernicus and Kepler to the present day.

Kline, Morris. *Mathematics: A Cultural Approach*. Reading, MA: Addison-Wesley Publishing Co., 1962. This survey of mathematics presents its topics in both historical and cultural settings, relating the ideas to the contexts in which they developed.

Priestley, William M. *Calculus: An Historical Approach*. New York, Heidelberg, and Berlin: Springer-Verlag, 1979. Develops the standard theory of calculus through discussions of its historical growth, emphasizing the history of ideas rather than the history of events.

Schey, H. M. *Div, Grad, Curl, and All That: An Informal Text on Vector Calculus*, 4th ed. New York: W.W. Norton, 2005. This book has been a favorite introduction to ideas of vector calculus for more than 30 years. It is short and clearly written. It presents vector calculus in the context of electrostatics, so it is especially attractive to people who have a feel for the physics of electricity and
magnetism.

Simmons, George F. *Calculus with Analytic Geometry*. New York: McGraw-Hill, 1985. This college-level mathematics text provides a standard development of calculus along with appendices that include biographical notes and supplementary topics.

Thompson, Sylvanus P., and Martin Gardner. *Calculus Made Easy*, New York: St. Martin's Press, 1998. This book is a revision, by the great mathematical expositor Martin Gardner, of a classical exposition of calculus for the general public.

Standard Textbooks

There are dozens of standard calculus and differential equations textbooks, usually titled *Calculus* and *Differential Equations*. Two of them are:

Boyce, William E., and Richard C. DiPrima. *Elementary Differential Equations and Boundary Value Problems*, 8th ed. New York: John Wiley & Sons, 2005. This is the bestselling introductory differential equations textbook. It presents differential equations from the applied mathematicians' point of view and includes explanations of both the theory and applications, as well as many examples, applications, and exercises.

Stewart, James. *Calculus*, 5th ed. Belmont, CA: Brooks/Cole, 2003. The Stewart textbook is the best-selling calculus textbook in the United States. It is well-written and comprehensive and contains many worked examples, applications, and exercises.

Internet Resources

A History of the Calculus. School of Mathematics and Statistics, University of St. Andrews, Scotland. www-history.mcs.st-andrews.ac.uk/history/HistTopics/The_rise_of_calculus.html. This site presents a synopsis of the history of calculus from ancient times through the time of Newton and Leibniz and includes links to many more history sites.

Index of Biographies. School of Mathematics and Statistics, University of St. Andrews, Scotland. www-history.mcs.st-andrews.ac.uk/~history/BiogIndex.html. This site contains biographical articles on many of the world's mathematicians from ancient times to the present. Both chronological and alphabetical indexes are presented, as well as such categories as famous curves, history topics, and so forth.

The Math Forum @ Drexel. Drexel School of Education, Drexel University. www.mathforum.org/library/topics/svcalc/. Includes links to many other sites that contain articles and demonstrations of concepts in calculus.

Mnatsakanian, Mamikon. *Visual Calculus by Mamikon*. California Institute of Technology. www.its.caltech.edu/~mamikon/calculus.html. This site offers animations demonstrating some of Mnatsakanian's applications of his clever sweeping tangent method for solving calculus problems.

Predator-Prey Models. Department of Mathematics, Duke University. www.math.duke.edu/education/webfeats/Word2HTML/Predator.html. This site provides an interactive location for creating direction fields and solutions to differential equation predator-prey models.

Weisstein, Eric. *Wolfram MathWorld, The Web's Most Extensive Mathematics Resource*. mathworld.wolfram.com. This website is like a mathematical encyclopedia. If you come across a mathematical term or concept, no matter how trivial or how involved, it's likely to be described here.